YORK NOTES

CW01021545

LOVE AND RELATIONSHIPS

AQA POETRY ANTHOLOGY

WORKBOOK BY MARY GREEN

YORK PRESS
322 Old Brompton Road, London SW5 9JH

PEARSON EDUCATION LIMITED
Edinburgh Gate, Harlow,
Essex CM20 2JE, United Kingdom
Associated companies, branches and representatives throughout the world

First published 2018

10 9 8 7 6 5 4 3 2 1

ISBN 978–1–2922–3680–3

Phototypeset by DTP Media
Printed in Slovakia

Text credits: 'Letters from Yorkshire' by Maura Dooley, from *Sound Barrier: Poems 1982–2002* (Bloodaxe
Books, 2002). Reproduced with permission of Bloodaxe Books. 'Walking Away' from *Selected Poems* by Cecil
Day Lewis reprinted by permission of Peters Fraser & Dunlop (www.petersfraserdunlop.com) on behalf of
the Estate of C. Day Lewis. 'Eden Rock' by Charles Causley from *Collected Poems*, Macmillan, 2000. 'Winter
Swans' from *Skirrid Hill* by Owen Sheers. Published by Seren, 2005. Copyright © Owen Sheers. Reproduced
by permission of the author c/o Rogers, Coleridge & White Ltd., 20 Powis Mews, London W11 1JN. 'Mother,
Any Distance' from *Book of Matches* by Simon Armitage and 'Singh Song!' from *Look We Have Coming to
Dover!* by Daljit Nagra reproduced by kind permission of Faber & Faber Ltd. 'Follower' from *Opened Ground:
Selected Poems 1966–1996* by Seamus Heaney. Copyright © 1998 by Seamus Heaney. Reprinted by permission
of Farrar, Straus and Giroux and of Faber and Faber Ltd. 'Before You Were Mine' by Carol Ann Duffy.
Copyright © Carol Ann Duffy. Reproduced by permission of Carol Ann Duffy c/o Rogers, Coleridge & White
Ltd., 20 Powis Mews, London W11 1JN. 'Climbing My Grandfather' by Andrew Waterhouse from *In*, Andrew
Waterhouse, The Rialto, 2000, reproduced by kind permission of The Rialto.

Photo credits: Vaclav Volrab/Shutterstock for page 11 / Zachary C Person/Shutterstock for page 16 / Josh Li/
Shutterstock for page 24 / SJ Travel Photo and Video/Shutterstock for page 30 / Ben Harding/Shutterstock for
page 36 / Halfpoint/iStock for page 40 / Roby1960/Shutterstock for page 45 / imagedb.com/Shutterstock for
page 50 / Artokoloro Quint Lox Limited/Alamy Stock Photo for page 56 / gyn9037/Shutterstock for page 59 /
Renata Sedmakova/Shutterstock for page 61

CONTENTS

PART FOUR:
FORM, STRUCTURE AND LANGUAGE

PART FIVE:
COMPARING POEMS

PART SIX:
PROGRESS BOOSTER

PART ONE: GETTING STARTED

Preparing for assessment

HOW WILL I BE ASSESSED ON MY WORK ON *LOVE AND RELATIONSHIPS*?

When studying the cluster, your work will be examined through these three Assessment Objectives:

Assessment Objectives	Wording	Worth thinking about …
AO1	Read, understand and respond to texts. Students should be able to: • maintain a critical style and develop an informed personal response • use textual references, including quotations, to support and illustrate interpretations.	• How well do I know what happens, what people say, do, etc. in each poem? • What do I think about the key ideas in the poems? • How can I support my viewpoint in a really convincing way? • What are the best quotations to use and when should I use them?
AO2	Analyse the language, form and structure used by a writer to create meanings and effects, using relevant subject terminology where appropriate.	• What specific things do the poets 'do'? What choices has each poet made? (Why this particular word, phrase or image here? Why does this change occur at this point?) • What effects do these choices create – optimism, pessimism, ambiguity?
AO3 *	Show understanding of the relationships between texts and the contexts in which they were written.	• What can I learn about society from the poems? (What do they tell me about stereotypes and prejudice, for example?) • What was/is society like for the poets? Can I see it reflected in their poems?

*AO3 is only assessed in relation to the cluster, and not in relation to the 'Unseen' part of the exam.

In other parts of your English Literature GCSE a fourth Assessment Objective, **AO4**, which is related to spelling, punctuation and grammar, is also assessed. While you will not gain any marks for AO4 in your poetry examination, it is still important to ensure that you write accurately and clearly in order to get your points across to the examiner in the best possible way.

Look out for the Assessment Objective labels throughout your York Notes Workbook – these will help to focus your study and revision!

The text used in this Workbook is *Past and Present: Poetry Anthology* (AQA, 2015).

How to use your York Notes Workbook

There are lots of ways your Workbook can support your study and revision of the *Love and Relationships* poetry cluster. There is no 'right' way – choose the one that suits your learning style best.

1) Alongside the York Notes Study Guide and the text	2) As a 'stand-alone' revision programme	3) As a form of mock-exam
Do you have the York Notes Study Guide for *Love and Relationships*?	Think you know *Love and Relationships* well?	Prefer to do all your revision in one go?
The contents of your Workbook are designed to match the sections in the Study Guide, so with the poems to hand you could:	Why not work through the Workbook systematically, either as you finish reading the poems, or as you study or revise certain aspects in class or at home.	You could put aside a day or two and work through the Workbook, page by page. Once you have finished, check all your answers in one go!
• read the relevant section(s) of the Study Guide and the poems referred to	You could make a revision diary and allocate particular sections of the Workbook to a day or week.	This will be quite a challenge, but it may be the approach you prefer.
• complete the tasks in the same section in your Workbook.		

HOW WILL THE WORKBOOK HELP YOU TEST AND CHECK YOUR KNOWLEDGE AND SKILLS?

Parts Two to **Five** offer a range of tasks and activities:

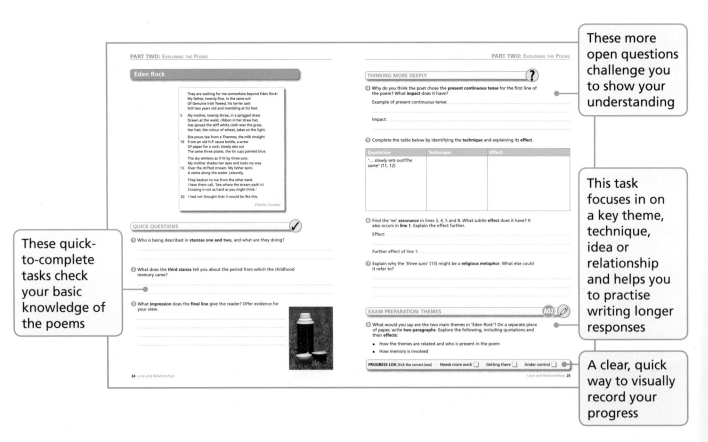

These more open questions challenge you to show your understanding

These quick-to-complete tasks check your basic knowledge of the poems

This task focuses in on a key theme, technique, idea or relationship and helps you to practise writing longer responses

A clear, quick way to visually record your progress

Each Part ends with a **Practice task** to extend your revision:

An exam-style task for you to practise a full essay

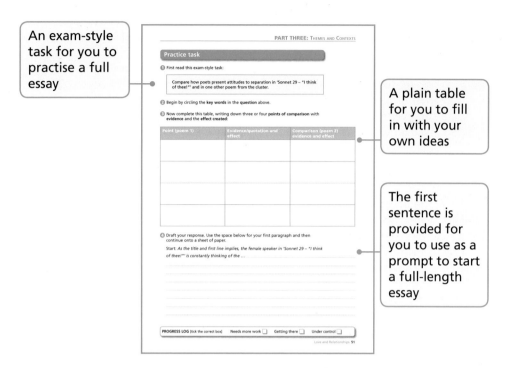

A plain table for you to fill in with your own ideas

The first sentence is provided for you to use as a prompt to start a full-length essay

Part Six: Progress Booster helps you test your own key writing skills:

A sample of a student's writing challenges you to judge its strengths and weaknesses

An expert teacher's or marker's view of the student's work to help you understand key skills

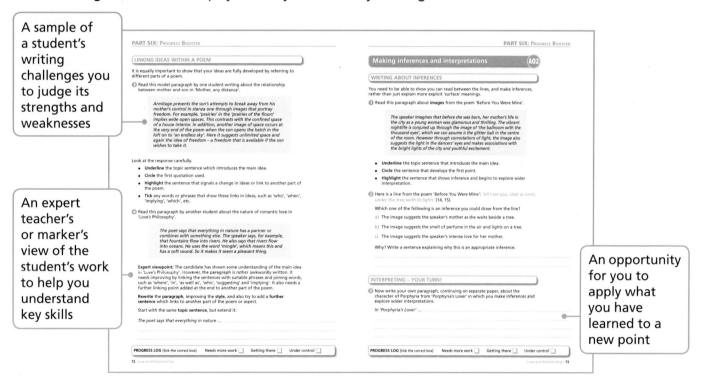

An opportunity for you to apply what you have learned to a new point

Don't forget – these are just some examples of the Workbook contents. Inside there is much, much more to help you revise. For example:

- top tips on approaching tricky questions
- help with comparing poems
- advice and tasks on writing about context
- a full-length sample answer for you to annotate and grade
- a full answer key so you can check your answers.

PART TWO: Exploring the Poems

When We Two Parted

> When we two parted
> In silence and tears,
> Half broken-hearted
> To sever for years,
> 5 Pale grew thy cheek and cold,
> Colder thy kiss;
> Truly that hour foretold
> Sorrow to this.
>
> The dew of the morning
> 10 Sunk chill on my brow –
> It felt like the warning
> Of what I feel now.
> Thy vows are all broken,
> And light is thy fame;
> 15 I hear thy name spoken,
> And share in its shame.
>
> They name thee before me,
> A knell in mine ear;
> A shudder comes o'er me –
> 20 Why wert thou so dear?
> They know not I knew thee,
> Who knew thee too well –
> Long, long shall I rue thee,
> Too deeply to tell.
>
> 25 In secret we met –
> In silence I grieve,
> That thy heart could forget,
> Thy spirit deceive.
> If I should meet thee
> 30 After long years,
> How should I greet thee? –
> With silence and tears.
>
> *Lord Byron*

QUICK QUESTIONS

1 What do the **title** and **first line** tell the reader the poem will be about?

....

....

2 Find a word that means 'cut' and describe its **effect**:

Word: ....

Effect: ....

....

3 Find the **metaphor** in stanza three and explain briefly what it implies.

....

....

THINKING MORE DEEPLY

4 Explain the poem's **circular structure** and what is conveyed.

....

....

....

....

5 How can you tell the poem belongs to the **Romantic period**? Find a **quotation** that tells you and explain how.

....

....

....

....

....

6 Complete the table below by identifying the **technique** used in the quotation and explaining the **effect**.

Quotation	Technique	Effect
'They know not I knew thee/Who knew thee too well –' (21, 22)		

7 What **themes** are suggested in lines 25 to 26 and how are they **related**? Use evidence to support your explanation.

The themes of … ....

....

....

....

....

....

EXAM PREPARATION: THEME AND FEELINGS   **A02** ✎

8 How would you describe the speaker's feelings about the loved one in 'When We Two Parted'? On a separate piece of paper, write **two paragraphs**. Explore the following, including quotations and their **effects**:

- the sense of **loss** and **separation** the speaker feels
- the sense of **betrayal** the speaker feels.

PROGRESS LOG [tick the correct box]   Needs more work ☐   Getting there ☐   Under control ☐

Love's Philosophy

> The fountains mingle with the river
> And the rivers with the Ocean,
> The winds of Heaven mix for ever
> With a sweet emotion;
> 5 Nothing in the world is single;
> All things by a law divine
> in one another's being mingle –
> Why not I with thine?
>
> See the mountains kiss high Heaven,
> 10 And the waves clasp one another;
> No sister-flower would be forgiven
> If it disdain'd its brother:
> And the sunlight clasps the earth,
> And the moonbeams kiss the sea –
> 15 what are all these kissings worth,
> If thou kiss not me?
>
> *Percey Bysshe Shelley*

QUICK QUESTIONS

1 Describe briefly what is happening in the **first two lines** of the poem.

....

....

2 What feeling is conveyed by the repeated **sibilant** ('s' sound) in the poem? Provide an **example** to support your point.

....

....

3 What does the **natural world** represent, and what **technique** is used to show this?

....

....

THINKING MORE DEEPLY

4 'Touch' is a key sense the poet uses. What **techniques** does the poet use in each of these cases? What is the **effect**?

Quotation: *'sunlight clasps the earth'* (13)

Technique: ....

Effect: ....

....

Quotation: *'moonbeams kiss the sea'* **(14)**

Technique: ....

Effect: ....

....

5 Find a quotation in the **second stanza** that depicts the female and nature together. What does it **convey**?

Quotation: ....

What it conveys: ....

....

....

6 Complete the table below by identifying the **technique** used in the quotation and explaining the **effect**.

Quotation	Technique	Effect
'high Heaven' (9)		

7 How does the poet present the **argument** in 'Love's Philosophy'? On a separate piece of paper, write **two paragraphs**, including quotations and their effects, and explore:

- how the structure of the poem relates to the argument
- how the rhythm and rhyme relate to the structure and argument.

PROGRESS LOG [tick the correct box]   Needs more work ☐   Getting there ☐   Under control ☐

Porphyria's Lover

The rain set early in to-night,
    The sullen wind was soon awake,
It tore the elm-tops down for spite,
    And did its worst to vex the lake:
5   I listened with heart fit to break.
When glided in Porphyria; straight
    She shut the cold out and the storm,
And kneeled and made the cheerless grate
    Blaze up, and all the cottage warm;
10   Which done, she rose, and from her form
Withdrew the dripping cloak and shawl,
    And laid her soiled gloves by, untied
Her hat and let the damp hair fall,
    And, last, she sat down by my side
15   And called me. When no voice replied,
She put my arm about her waist,
    And made her smooth white shoulder bare,
And all her yellow hair displaced,
    And, stooping, made my cheek lie there,
20   And spread, o'er all, her yellow hair,
Murmuring how she loved me – she
    Too weak, for all her heart's endeavour,
To set its struggling passion free
    From pride, and vainer ties dissever,
25   And give herself to me for ever.
But passion sometimes would prevail,
    Nor could tonight's gay feast restrain
A sudden thought of one so pale
    For love of her, and all in vain:
30   So, she was come through wind and rain.
Be sure I looked up at her eyes

    Happy and proud; at last I knew
Porphyria worshipped me: surprise
    Made my heart swell, and still it grew
35   While I debated what to do.
That moment she was mine, mine, fair,
    Perfectly pure and good: I found
A thing to do, and all her hair
    In one long yellow string I wound
40   Three times her little throat around,
And strangled her. No pain felt she;
    I am quite sure she felt no pain.
As a shut bud that holds a bee,
    I warily oped her lids: again
45   Laughed the blue eyes without a stain.
And I untightened next the tress
    About her neck; her cheek once more
Blushed bright beneath my burning kiss:
    I propped her head up as before,
50   Only, this time my shoulder bore
Her head, which droops upon it still:
    The smiling rosy little head,
So glad it has its utmost will,
    That all it scorned at once is fled,
55   And I, its love, am gained instead!
Porphyria's love: she guessed not how
    Her darling one wish would be heard.
And thus we sit together now,
    And all night long we have not stirred,
60   And yet God has not said a word!

Robert Browning

QUICK QUESTIONS

❶ What **form** of poem is 'Porphyria's Lover'?

....

....

❷ Find an example of **pathetic fallacy** in lines 2 to 4, and briefly describe its **impact**.

Example: ....

Impact: ....

....

❸ What do *'cloak and shawl'* (11) *'gloves'* (12) and *'hat'* (13) tell you about
Porphyria's status?

....

....

THINKING MORE DEEPLY   **?**

4 What do you learn about **Porphyria** in lines 6 to 9? What impression does she give?

As she enters the cottage, Porphyria creates the impression ... .

....

....

....

....

5 Complete the table below by identifying each of the **techniques** and explaining their **effects**.

Quotation	Technique	Effect
'The rain set early in to-night' (1)		
'vainer ties' (24)		

6 Why is the poem's final line **ambiguous**? What do you think it could mean?

....

....

....

....

....

EXAM PREPARATION: CONTRASTS WITHIN A POEM   **A02** 🖊

7 How are the speaker and Porphyria contrasted in 'Porphyria's Lover'? On a separate piece of paper, write **two paragraphs** describing:

- what the relationship is like in the first half of the poem (up to line 30)
- how the relationship changes in the second half (line 31 to the end).

PROGRESS LOG [tick the correct box]   Needs more work ☐   Getting there ☐   Under control ☐

Sonnet 29 – 'I think of thee!'

> I think of thee! – my thoughts do twine and bud
> About thee, as wild vines, about a tree,
> Put out broad leaves, and soon there's nought to see
> Except the straggling green which hides the wood.
> 5   Yet, O my palm-tree, be it understood
> I will not have my thoughts instead of thee
> Who art dearer, better! Rather, instantly
> Renew thy presence; as a strong tree should,
> Rustle thy boughs and set thy trunk all bare,
> 10 And let these bands of greenery which insphere thee
> Drop heavily down, – burst, shattered, everywhere!
> Because, in this deep joy to see and hear thee
> And breathe within thy shadow a new air,
> I do not think of thee – I am too near thee.
>
> *Elizabeth Barrett Browning*

QUICK QUESTIONS

1 How can you tell the poem is not a modern poem? Find **two examples** in lines 1 to 3 and briefly explain why.

   a) Quotation: ....

   ....

   Explanation: ....

   ....

   b) Quotation: ....

   ....

   Explanation: ....

   ....

2 Find a quotation in line 5 that describes the **male lover**, and briefly explain why it has been used.

   Quotation: ....

   ....

   Explanation: ....

   ....

3 Find an example of **alliteration** in line 11, and describe the **sound** it creates.

   ....

   ....

THINKING MORE DEEPLY ?

4 What do you learn about the speaker's **voice** from the first words, 'I think of thee!'?

....

....

....

5 In the quotation below explain what **technique** the poet is using, and its **effect**.

Quotation: *'my thoughts do twine and bud/About thee, as wild vines, about a tree'* (1, 2)

Technique: ....

Effect: ....

....

....

....

6 Separation is a **main theme** in the poem. Provide evidence to support this:

Evidence: ....

....

....

....

7 What kind of **imagery** is used throughout the poem? Describe its **effect** in line 9.

Imagery: ....

....

Effect: ....

....

....

EXAM PREPARATION: FORM AND STRUCTURE (A02) ✎

8 How would you describe the **form and structure** of 'Sonnet 29 – "I think of thee!"'? On a separate piece of paper, write **two paragraphs**. Include quotations and their **effects**, and explore:

- how the poem is laid out, and what kind of sonnet the poem is
- how the underlying pattern of the poem shows the development of the poet's ideas.

PROGRESS LOG [tick the correct box]   Needs more work ☐   Getting there ☐   Under control ☐

Neutral Tones

> We stood by a pond that winter day,
> And the sun was white, as though chidden of God,
> And a few leaves lay on the starving sod;
>   – They had fallen from an ash, and were grey.
>
> 5   Your eyes on me were as eyes that rove
> Over tedious riddles of years ago;
> And some words played between us to and fro
>   On which lost the more by our love.
>
> The smile on your mouth was the deadest thing
> 10 Alive enough to have strength to die;
> And a grin of bitterness swept thereby
>   Like an ominous bird a-wing…
>
> Since then, keen lessons that love deceives,
> And wrings with wrong, have shaped to me
> 15 Your face, and the God curst sun, and a tree,
>   And a pond edged with greyish leaves.
>
> *Thomas Hardy*

QUICK QUESTIONS

1 Briefly describe what is happening to the speaker in the **first stanza** of the poem.

....

....

2 Find an example of a **simile** in the **third stanza** and briefly describe its **effect**.

Simile: ....

....

Effect: ....

....

THINKING MORE DEEPLY

3 What is the **main theme** in the poem? Support your answer with with quotations.

....

....

....

....

....

4 Where in line 7 is the rhythm lost? What is the impact of this?

....

....

....

....

....

5 Complete the table below by identifying each of the **techniques** and explaining their **effects**.

Quotation	Technique	Effect
'And some words played between us to and fro/On which lost the more by our love' (7, 8)		
'eyes that rove/Over tedious riddles ...' (5, 6)		

EXAM PREPARATION: COMPARISONS BETWEEN POEMS (A02) ✎

6 Read 'Love's Philosophy'. On a separate piece of paper, write **two paragraphs** comparing the **speaker's attitude** to relationships in this poem and in 'Neutral Tones'. Include:

- at least one quotation from each poem which shows their viewpoint with an explanation
- exploration of how nature imagery is used for effect in these poems.

PROGRESS LOG [tick the correct box]   Needs more work ☐   Getting there ☐   Under control ☐

Letters from Yorkshire

In February, digging his garden, planting potatoes,
he saw the first lapwings return and came
indoors to write to me, his knuckles singing

as they reddened in the warmth.
5   It's not romance, simply how things are.
You out there, in the cold, seeing the seasons

turning, me with my heartful of headlines
feeding words onto a blank screen.
Is your life more real because you dig and sow?

10   You wouldn't say so, breaking ice on a waterbutt,
clearing a path through snow. Still, it's you
who sends me word of that other world

pouring air and light into an envelope. So that
at night, watching the same news in different houses,
15   our souls tap out messages across the icy miles.

Maura Dooley

QUICK QUESTIONS

1. How do you know from **very** early on in the poem that the speaker and the friend are not living in the same place? Give an **example** and explain.

....

....

2. Find an example of **alliteration** in the first stanza, and briefly describe what the **sound** reminds you of.

Example: ....

....

Effect: ....

....

3. Find a quotation in stanza four in which **colloquial speech** is used. What impression does it give of the speaker's **tone**?

Quotation: ....

....

....

Impression: ....

....

....

....

THINKING MORE DEEPLY   **?**

4 In the quotation below, name the **two sound techniques** used and describe **their combined effect**.

Quotation: *'seeing the seasons'* (6)

Technique 1: ....

Technique 2: ....

Combined effect: ....

....

5 What happens to the **viewpoint** in line 6? Explain the **impact** of this on the reader.

....

....

....

....

....

6 What do you think *'heartful of headlines'* (7) means? Think of **more than one possibility**.

....

....

....

....

....

7 Find the **rhyme** in stanza four. What **type** is this? Describe its **effect**.

Rhyme: ....

Type: ....

Effect: ....

....

EXAM PREPARATION: RELATIONSHIPS AND THEME   **A02** ✐

8 How would you describe the relationship between the speaker and the friend in 'Letters from Yorkshire'? On a separate piece of paper, write **two paragraphs**. Explore the following, including quotations and their **effects**:

- How their lives are different
- The importance of communication

PROGRESS LOG [tick the correct box]   Needs more work ☐   Getting there ☐   Under control ☐

The Farmer's Bride

Three Summers since I chose a maid,
Too young maybe – but more's to do
At harvest-time than bide and woo.
   When us was wed she turned afraid
5 Of love and me and all things human;
Like the shut of a winter's day
Her smile went out, and 'twasn't a woman –
   More like a little frightened fay.
   One night, in the Fall, she runned away.

10 'Out 'mong the sheep, her be,' they said,
Should properly have been abed;
But sure enough she wasn't there
Lying awake with her wide brown stare.
   So over seven-acre field and up-along across the down
15 We chased her, flying like a hare
Before our lanterns. To Church-Town
   All in a shiver and a scare
We caught her, fetched her home at last
   And turned the key upon her, fast.

20 She does the work about the house
As well as most, but like a mouse:
   Happy enough to chat and play
   With birds and rabbits and such as they,
So long as men-folk keep away.

25 'Not near, not near!' her eyes beseech
When one of us comes within reach.
   The women say that beasts in stall
   Look round like children at her call.
   I've hardly heard her speak at all.

30 Shy as a leveret, swift as he,
Straight and slight as a young larch tree,
Sweet as the first wild violets, she,
To her wild self. But what to me?

The short days shorten and the oaks are brown,
35   The blue smoke rises to the low grey sky,
One leaf in the still air falls slowly down,
   A magpie's spotted feathers lie
On the black earth spread white with rime,
The berries redden up to Christmas-time.
40   What's Christmas-time without there be
   Some other in the house than we!

   She sleeps up in the attic there
   Alone, poor maid. 'Tis but a stair
Betwixt us. Oh! my God! the down,
45 The soft young down of her, the brown,
The brown of her – her eyes, her hair, her hair!

Charlotte Mew

QUICK QUESTIONS

1 From whose **viewpoint** is the poem told? Find an **example** to support what you say.

Viewpoint: ....

Example: ....

....

2 What **tense** does the poem shift to in line 20? What is the **effect**?

Tense: ....

....

Effect: ....

....

3 Find a **metaphor** for blood and a reference to birth between lines 35 and 40.
Briefly explain why you think these are used.

....

....

....

THINKING MORE DEEPLY **?**

④ Into what **forms** of poetry do you think 'The Farmer's Bride' fits? Give **two** examples, and offer **evidence** of your choice for each.

a) ....

....

b) ....

....

⑤ Complete the table below by identifying each of the **techniques** and explaining their **effects**.

Quotation	Technique	Effect
'Too young maybe –' (2)		
'Sweet as the first wild violets, she' (32)		

⑥ What does the **image** in lines 37 and 38 depict? What does it **suggest**?

....

....

....

....

EXAM PREPARATION: RELATIONSHIPS AND ATTITUDES **A02** ✎

⑦ How would you describe the relationship between the farmer and his wife in 'The Farmer's Bride'? On a separate piece of paper, write **two paragraphs**. Explore the following, including quotations and their **effects**:

● His attitude to her

● Her attitude to him and others

PROGRESS LOG [tick the correct box] Needs more work ☐ Getting there ☐ Under control ☐

Walking Away

It is eighteen years ago, almost to the day –
A sunny day with leaves just turning,
The touch-lines new-ruled – since I watched you play
Your first game of football, then, like a satellite
5   Wrenched from its orbit, go drifting away

Behind a scatter of boys. I can see
You walking away from me towards the school
With the pathos of a half-fledged thing set free
Into a wilderness, the gait of one
10 Who finds no path where the path should be.

That hesitant figure, eddying away
Like a winged seed loosened from its parent stem,
Has something I never quite grasp to convey
About nature's give-and-take – the small, the scorching
15 Ordeals which fire one's irresolute clay.

I have had worse partings, but none that so
Gnaws at my mind still. Perhaps it is roughly
Saying what God alone could perfectly show –
How selfhood begins with a walking away,
20 And love is proved in the letting go.

Cecil Day Lewis

QUICK QUESTIONS

1 What **mood** might be conveyed by the **first two lines**?

....

....

2 The word 'away' is repeated throughout the poem. Find three **examples**, and suggest what **theme** it represents.

Example 1: ....

Example 2: ....

Example 3: ....

Theme: ....

....

3 What do you think **the poet means** by *'the small, the scorching/Ordeals'* (14, 15)?

....

....

THINKING MORE DEEPLY

4 Complete the table below by identifying each of the **techniques** and explaining their **effects**.

Quotation	Technique	Effect
'like a satellite/Wrenched from its orbit' (4, 5)		
'irresolute clay' (15)		

5 Why does the poet use **enjambment** in lines 16 and 17? Describe its **impact**.

....

....

....

....

6 What does the speaker **have difficulty conveying** in line 13? How does he manage to do this?

....

....

....

....

EXAM PREPARATION: VIEWPOINT A02

7 How would you describe the child in 'Walking Away'? On a separate piece of paper, write **two paragraphs**. Explore the following, including quotations and their **effects**:

- From whose viewpoint the child is described, and where the child is
- What changes are occurring in the child's life

PROGRESS LOG [tick the correct box]   Needs more work ☐   Getting there ☐   Under control ☐

Eden Rock

> They are waiting for me somewhere beyond Eden Rock:
> My father, twenty-five, in the same suit
> Of Genuine Irish Tweed, his terrier Jack
> Still two years old and trembling at his feet.
>
> 5   My mother, twenty-three, in a sprigged dress
> Drawn at the waist, ribbon in her straw hat,
> Has spread the stiff white cloth over the grass.
> Her hair, the colour of wheat, takes on the light.
>
> She pours tea from a Thermos, the milk straight
> 10 From an old H.P. sauce bottle, a screw
> Of paper for a cork; slowly sets out
> The same three plates, the tin cups painted blue.
>
> The sky whitens as if lit by three suns.
> My mother shades her eyes and looks my way
> 15 Over the drifted stream. My father spins
> A stone along the water. Leisurely,
>
> They beckon to me from the other bank.
> I hear them call, 'See where the stream-path is!
> Crossing is not as hard as you might think.'
>
> 20 I had not thought that it would be like this.

Charles Causley

QUICK QUESTIONS

1 Who is being described in **stanzas one and two,** and what are they doing?

....

....

2 What does the **third stanza** tell you about the period from which the childhood memory came?

....

....

3 What **impression** does the **final line** give the reader? Offer evidence for your view.

....

....

....

....

THINKING MORE DEEPLY ?

4 Why do you think the poet chose the **present continuous tense** for the first line of the poem? What **impact** does it have?

Example of present continuous tense: ....

....

Impact: ....

....

5 Complete the table below by identifying the **technique** and explaining its **effect**.

Quotation	Technique	Effect
'... slowly sets out/The same' (11, 12)		

6 Find the 'ee' **assonance** in lines 3, 4, 5 and 8. What subtle **effect** does it have? It also occurs in **line 1**. Explain the effect further.

Effect: ....

....

Further effect of line 1: ....

7 Explain why the *'three suns'* (13) might be a **religious metaphor**. What else could it refer to?

....

....

....

EXAM PREPARATION: THEMES (A02) 🖊

8 What would you say are the two main themes in 'Eden Rock'? On a separate piece of paper, write **two paragraphs**. Explore the following, including quotations and their **effects**:

- How the themes are related and who is present in the poem
- How memory is involved

PROGRESS LOG [tick the correct box]   Needs more work ☐   Getting there ☐   Under control ☐

Follower

My father worked with a horse-plough,
His shoulders globed like a full sail strung
Between the shafts and the furrow.
The horse strained at his clicking tongue.

5   An expert. He would set the wing
And fit the bright steel-pointed sock.
The sod rolled over without breaking.
At the headrig, with a single pluck

Of reins, the sweating team turned round
10 And back into the land. His eye
Narrowed and angled at the ground,
Mapping the furrow exactly.

I stumbled in his hob-nailed wake,
Fell sometimes on the polished sod;
15 Sometimes he rode me on his back
Dipping and rising to his plod.

I wanted to grow up and plough,
To close one eye, stiffen my arm.
All I ever did was follow
20 In his broad shadow round the farm.

I was a nuisance, tripping, falling,
Yapping always. But today
It is my father who keeps stumbling
Behind me, and will not go away.

Seamus Heaney

QUICK QUESTIONS

1 Who does the **title** of the poem apply to?

....

....

2 Briefly describe what is happening in the **first stanza**.

....

....

3 Find the quotation that **depicts** how the **child** tries to **imitate** his father's skill, and explain this.

Quotation: ....

....

Explanation: ....

....

THINKING MORE DEEPLY ❓

4️⃣ How are the **movements of the plough** depicted in the verse pattern, and what does it **convey**?

The regular verse pattern … ....

....

....

This pattern is broken by … ....

....

....

5️⃣ Complete the example by identifying the **metre** and explaining its **effect**.

Example of metre: *'I stumbled in his hob-nailed wake'* (13)

Type of metre: ....

Effect: ....

....

....

6️⃣ Find an example of **full rhyme** and **half rhyme** in **stanza five**. How do they suit the **metre**?

....

....

....

....

7️⃣ The word *'wake'* (13) is used. What **relevant meanings** does it have, and what **effects** does it create?

Meaning 1 and effect: ....

....

Meaning 2 and effect: ....

....

EXAM PREPARATION: VIEWPOINT AND CHANGE (A02) ✏️

8️⃣ How would you describe the relationship between the son and his father in 'Follower'? On a separate piece of paper, write **two paragraphs**. Explore the following, including quotations and their **effects**:

- The child's view of his father
- How the father/son relationship changes and develops

PROGRESS LOG [tick the correct box]   Needs more work ☐   Getting there ☐   Under control ☐

Mother, any distance

Mother, any distance greater than a single span
requires a second pair of hands.
You come to help me measure windows, pelmets, doors,
the acres of the walls, the prairies of the floors.

5   You at the zero-end, me with the spool of tape, recording
length, reporting metres, centimetres back to base, then leaving
up the stairs, the line still feeding out, unreeling
years between us. Anchor. Kite.

I space-walk through the empty bedrooms, climb
10   the ladder to the loft, to breaking point, where something
has to give;
two floors below your fingertips still pinch
the last one-hundredth of an inch ... I reach
towards a hatch that opens on an endless sky
15   to fall or fly.

Simon Armitage

QUICK QUESTIONS

1 Briefly describe the setting in the **first stanza**.

....

....

2 Explain the **double meaning** of the following quotation:

Quotation: *'unreeling/years between us'* (7, 8)

Meaning 1: ....

....

Meaning 2: ....

....

3 Find an example of a **compound word** between **lines 6 and 9,** and describe its **impact**.

Example: ....

Impact: ....

....

THINKING MORE DEEPLY ?

4 Explain the meaning of the first two lines. What does it tell you about the mother and the son?

Meaning: ....

....

Effect: ....

....

5 Complete the table below by identifying each of the **techniques** and explaining their **effects**.

Quotation	Technique	Effect
'something/has to give' (10, 11)		
'fingertips still pinch' (12)		

6 How is the tape measure reflected in the poem's form?

....

....

....

....

EXAM PREPARATION: COMPARISONS BETWEEN POEMS A02

7 Read 'Follower'. On a separate piece of paper, write **two paragraphs** comparing the speaker's attitude to his father in 'Follower' with the speaker's attitude to his mother in 'Mother, any distance'. Include:

- at least one quotation from each poem which shows their attitude
- an explanation of what these quotations tell us about the speakers' attitudes and relationships.

PROGRESS LOG [tick the correct box]   Needs more work ☐   Getting there ☐   Under control ☐

Before You Were Mine

I'm ten years away from the corner you laugh on
with your pals, Maggie McGeeney and Jean Duff.
The three of you bend from the waist, holding
each other, or your knees, and shriek at the pavement.
5   Your polka-dot dress blows round your legs. Marilyn.

I'm not here yet. The thought of me doesn't occur
in the ballroom with the thousand eyes, the fizzy, movie tomorrows
the right walk home could bring. I knew you would dance
like that. Before you were mine, your Ma stands at the close
10   with a hiding for the late one. You reckon it's worth it.

The decade ahead of my loud, possessive yell was the best one, eh?
I remember my hands in those high-heeled red shoes, relics,
and now your ghost clatters toward me over George Square
till I see you, clear as scent, under the tree,
15   with its lights, and whose small bites on your neck, sweetheart?

Cha cha cha! You'd teach me the steps on the way home from Mass,
stamping stars from the wrong pavement. Even then
I wanted the bold girl winking in Portobello, somewhere
in Scotland, before I was born. That glamorous love lasts
20   where you sparkle and waltz and laugh before you were mine.

Carol Ann Duffy

QUICK QUESTIONS

1 Find a **quotation** that **suggests** a rotating glitterball in **stanza 2**.

....

....

2 Select two techniques from the box below that are used in these
lines from **stanza two**:

'I knew you would dance/like that' (8, 9).

enjambment	internal rhyme	
oxymoron	couplet	caesura	motif

Technique 1: ....

Technique 2: ....

3 Find a quotation in **stanza two** that means 'a beating', and briefly describe the
impression it creates.

....

....

THINKING MORE DEEPLY ?

❹ Find a quotation in the **first stanza** that gives a clue to the **historical period** in which the mother was young. Explain it, and describe the **mood** it creates.

Quotation: ....

....

Historical period: ....

....

Explanation: ....

....

❺ Complete the table below by identifying the **techniques** and explaining their **effects**.

Quotation	Technique	Effect
'the fizzy, movie tomorrows' (7)		.
'stamping stars' (17)		

❻ Find an **image** in **line 14** that appeals to more than the sense of sight, and describe the **effects** it creates.

Image: ....

....

Effect 1: ....

....

Effect 2: ....

....

EXAM PREPARATION: POETIC STRUCTURE AND VOICE (A02) ✎

❼ How is 'Before You Were Mine' structured? On a separate piece of paper, write **two paragraphs**. Explore the following, including quotations and their **effects**:

● The voice of the speaker

● The ending of the poem

PROGRESS LOG [tick the correct box]   Needs more work ☐   Getting there ☐   Under control ☐

Winter Swans

The clouds had given their all –
two days of rain and then a break
in which we walked,

the waterlogged earth
5   gulping for breath at our feet
as we skirted the lake, silent and apart,

until the swans came and stopped us
with a show of tipping in unison.
As if rolling weights down their bodies to their heads

10   they halved themselves in the dark water,
icebergs of white feather, paused before returning again
like boats righting in rough weather.

'They mate for life' you said as they left,
porcelain over the stilling water. I didn't reply
15   but as we moved on through the afternoon light,

slow-stepping in the lake's shingle and sand,
I noticed our hands, that had, somehow,
swum the distance between us

and folded, one over the other,
20   like a pair of wings settling after flight.

Owen Sheers

QUICK QUESTIONS

1 From whose **viewpoint** is the poem told, and addressed **to whom**?

....

....

2 Find a quotation in **stanza three** that describes how the swans behave. What **feeling or emotion** is conveyed?

Quotation: ....

Feeling/emotion: ....

....

3 Find an example of the **sibilant** in **stanza six**, and describe its **effect**.

Example: ....

....

Effect: ....

....

THINKING MORE DEEPLY ?

4 What kind of verse form is used in **stanzas one to six**? Give an example, and explain its **impact**.

....

....

....

....

....

5 What does the **quotation** *'gulping for breath'* (5) **convey** about the relationship?

....

....

....

....

....

6 For each of the quotations below, explain the **technique** the poet is using and its **effect**.

Quotation	Technique	Effect
'The clouds had given their all' (1)		
The swans like *'porcelain'* (14)		

EXAM PREPARATION: RELATIONSHIPS AND MOTIF A02

7 How would you describe the relationship between the speaker and his partner in 'Winter Swans'? On a separate piece of paper, write **two paragraphs**. Explore the following, including quotations and their **effects**:

- The situation at the beginning of the poem
- The motif of the swans' relationship and its significance

PROGRESS LOG [tick the correct box]   Needs more work ☐   Getting there ☐   Under control ☐

Singh Song!

I run just one ov my daddy's shops
from 9 o'clock to 9 o'clock
and he vunt me not to hav a break
but ven nobody in, I do di lock –

5   cos up di stairs is my newly bride
vee share in chapatti
vee share in di chutney
after vee hav made luv
like vee rowing through Putney –

10 Ven I return vid my pinnie untied
di shoppers always point and cry:
Hey Singh, ver yoo bin?
Yor lemons are limes
yor bananas are plantain,
15 *dis dirty little floor need a little bit of mop*
in di worst Indian shop
on di whole Indian road –

Above my head high heel tap di ground
as my vife on di web is playing wid di mouse
20 ven she netting two cat on her Sikh lover site
she book dem for di meat at di cheese ov her price –

my bride
   she effing at my mum
   in all di colours of Punjabi
25   den stumble like a drunk
   making fun at my daddy

my bride
   tiny eyes ov a gun
   and di tummy ov a teddy

30 my bride
   she hav a red crew cut
   and she wear a Tartan sari
   a donkey jacket and some pumps
   on di squeak ov di girls dat are pinching my sweeties –

35 Ven I return from di tickle ov my bride
di shoppers always point and cry:
Hey Singh, ver yoo bin?
Di milk is out ov date
and di bread is alvays stale,
40 *di tings yoo hav on offer yoo hav never got in stock*
in di worst Indian shop
on di whole Indian road –

Late in di midnight hour
ven yoo shoppers are wrap up quiet
45 ven di precinct is concrete-cool
vee cum down whispering stairs
and sit on my silver stool,
from behind di chocolate bars
vee stare past di half-price window signs
50 at di beaches ov di UK in di brightey moon –

from di stool each night she say,
   How much do yoo charge for dat moon baby?

from di stool each night I say,
   Is half di cost ov yoo baby,

55 from di stool each night she say,
   How much does dat come to baby?

from di stool each night I say,
   Is priceless baby –

Daljit Nagra

QUICK QUESTIONS

1 What does the speaker tell us at the **start** of the poem?

....

....

2 Look at the use of **internal rhyme** in lines 12 and 37. Describe the **mood** it creates.

Internal rhyme: ....

Mood: ....

3 Why do you think **caesura** is used so much in 'Singh Song!'? Explain briefly.

....

....

THINKING MORE DEEPLY **?**

4 What **mood** does the **chorus** create?

....

....

....

....

5 Complete the table below by identifying each of the **techniques** and explaining their **effects**.

Quotation	Technique	Effect
'Singh' (title)		
'pinnie' (10)		

6 Why do you think 'vee' is repeated so often in **stanza two**? What **impact** does it make?

....

....

....

....

EXAM PREPARATION: WRITING ABOUT VIEWPOINT **A02** ✎

7 How does the speaker in 'Singh Song!' describe his bride? On a separate piece of paper, write **two paragraphs**. Explore the following, including quotations and their **effects**:

• Her character and nature

• Her attitude to marriage

PROGRESS LOG [tick the correct box]   Needs more work ☐   Getting there ☐   Under control ☐

Climbing My Grandfather

I decide to do it free, without a rope or net.
First, the old brogues, dusty and cracked;
an easy scramble onto his trousers,
pushing into the weave, trying to get a grip.
5   By the overhanging shirt I change
direction, traverse along his belt
to an earth-stained hand. The nails
are splintered and give good purchase,
the skin of his finger is smooth and thick
10   like warm ice. On his arm I discover
the glassy ridge of a scar, place my feet
gently in the old stitches and move on.
At his still firm shoulder, I rest for a while
in the shade, not looking down,
15   for climbing has its dangers, then pull
myself up the loose skin of his neck
to a smiling mouth to drink among teeth.
Refreshed, I cross the screed cheek,
to stare into his brown eyes, watch a pupil
20   slowly open and close. Then up over
the forehead, the wrinkles well-spaced
and easy, to his thick hair (soft and white
at this altitude), reaching for the summit,
where gasping for breath I can only lie
25   watching clouds and birds circle,
feeling his heat, knowing
the slow pulse of his good heart.

Andrew Waterhouse

QUICK QUESTIONS ✓

1 What picture does the poem's **title** conjure up?

....

....

What **impression** do you gain of the **grandfather** in **lines 7 and 8**?

....

....

....

....

3 Why is the **form** (or shape) of the poem suited to the poem's meaning?

....

....

....

THINKING MORE DEEPLY ❓

4 What do you learn about the start of the **climb** in the **second line**, and what does it **imply**?

....

....

....

....

5 How do the **geographical terms** help to build the extended metaphor of the climb? Find an **example** and say how it contributes to the poem's **impact**.

....

....

....

....

6 Complete the table below by identifying the **techniques** and explaining their **effects**.

Quotation	Technique	Effect
'belt' (6)		
'stare into his brown eyes, watch a pupil/slowly open and close' (19, 20)		

EXAM PREPARATION: WRITING ABOUT POETIC STRCTURE (A02) ✏️

7 How is 'Climbing My Grandfather' structured? On a separate piece of paper, write **two paragraphs**. Explore the following, including quotations and their **effects**:

- How climbing the mountain helps to structure the poem
- What the climb might mean for the speaker

PROGRESS LOG [tick the correct box]   Needs more work ☐   Getting there ☐   Under control ☐

Practice task

1 First read this exam-style task:

> Compare how poets present attitudes to friends or lovers in 'Letters from Yorkshire' and in one other poem from the *Love and Relationships* cluster.

2 Begin by circling the **key words** in the **question** above.

3 Now complete this table, writing down three or four **points of comparison**, with **evidence** and the **effect each creates**:

Point (poem 1)	Evidence/quotation and effect	Comparison (poem 2) evidence and effect

4 Draft your **response**. Use the space below for your first paragraph and then continue on a sheet of paper.

Start: *In 'Letters from Yorkshire' the speaker addresses the reader as though she is talking about a friend, telling us that …*

....

....

....

....

....

....

....

....

....

....

....

PROGRESS LOG [tick the correct box]   Needs more work ☐   Getting there ☐   Under control ☐

PART THREE: THEMES AND CONTEXTS

Themes: Breakdown and betrayal

QUICK QUESTION ✔

1 What does the **title** 'Neutral Tones' tell you about the **theme** of **relationship breakdown**?

....

....

THINKING MORE DEEPLY ?

2 Explain the **effect** of the clouds as an **image** of **relationship breakdown** in line 1 of 'Winter Swans'.

....

....

....

....

3 Explain how the quotations below relate to the **themes** of either **betrayal** or **relationship breakdown**.

a) Quotation from 'The Farmer's Bride': *'Like the shut of a winter's day'* (6)

Link to theme: ....

....

....

Effect: ....

....

....

b) Quotation from 'When We Two Parted': *'That thy heart could forget,/Thy spirit deceive'* (27, 28)

Link to theme: ....

....

....

Effect: ....

....

....

| **PROGRESS LOG** [tick the correct box] | Needs more work ☐ | Getting there ☐ | Under control ☐ |

Themes: Family ties

QUICK QUESTION ✔

❶ Which poem is written from the **perspective of the father**, and **about whom**?

....

....

THINKING MORE DEEPLY ❓

❷ How does the **image** *'The same three plates, the tin cups painted blue'* (12) **convey** the **theme** of **family ties** in 'Eden Rock'? Use **evidence** to support your answer.

....

....

....

❸ For each of the quotations below, explain how it relates to the **theme** of **family ties** and show its **effect**.

a) Quotation from 'Follower': *'I stumbled in his hob-nailed wake'* (13)

Link to theme: ....

....

Effect: ....

....

....

b) Quotation from 'Before You were Mine': *'Even then/I wanted the bold girl winking in Portobello'* (17, 18)

Link to theme: ....

....

....

Effect: ....

....

....

....

....

④ Find a quotation in **lines 11 and 12** from 'Climbing My Grandfather' that describes the theme of **family ties**, and complete the table.

Quotation	Effect

⑤ Find a quotation from the **first stanza** of 'Eden Rock' that describes the theme of **family ties**, and complete the table.

Quotation	Effect

EXAM PREPARATION: COMPARING THEMES (A02) ✎

⑥ Explain how both parents find it difficult to let go in 'Walking Away' and 'Mother, any distance'. Write **two paragraphs**. Make sure you include **two or more** quotations from each poem, and include the **effect** on the reader.

Use the space below for your first paragraph and then continue onto a separate sheet of paper.

....

....

....

....

....

....

....

....

....

....

TOP TIP (A01)

If you are asked to write about family relationships in the exam, remember to consider whether and how the relationship changes, from the beginning to the end of the poem, as it does in 'Follower'.

PROGRESS LOG [tick the correct box]   Needs more work ☐   Getting there ☐   Under control ☐

Themes: Love and desire

QUICK QUESTION ✔

❶ In which two poems is the **speaker's love not returned**? Who are the relationships between?

a) ....

b) ....

THINKING MORE DEEPLY ❓

❷ Would you describe the relationship in 'Letters from Yorkshire' as **romantic love, or not**? Use **evidence** to support your answer.

....

....

....

....

....

❸ In the quotations below, **explain** how they relate to the **theme**, and describe their **effects**.

a) Quotation from 'Love's Philosophy': *'what are all these kissings worth,/If thou kiss not me?'* (15, 16)

Link to theme: ....

....

Effect: ....

....

b) Quotation from 'Sonnet 29 – "I think of thee!"': *'I will not have my thoughts instead of thee'* (6)

Link to theme: ....

....

Effect: ....

....

④ Find a quotation from **lines 30 to 34** of 'Porphyria's Lover' that describes the speaker's **delusion about love**, and complete the table.

Quotation	Effect

⑤ Find a quotation from **stanza six** of 'Winter Swans' that describes being reunited in love, and complete the table.

Quotation	Effect

EXAM PREPARATION: COMPARING THEMES (A02) ✎

⑥ Explain how the speakers in 'The Farmer's Bride' and 'Singh Song!' describe their **marriages**. Write **two paragraphs**. Make sure you include **two or more** quotations from each poem, and include the **effect** on the reader.

Use the space below for your first paragraph and then continue onto a separate sheet of paper.

....

....

....

....

....

....

....

TOP TIP (A01)

All the poems in the cluster concerned with love and desire explore its nature and complexity. For example, think about the destructive nature of love in 'Porphyria's Lover'.

PROGRESS LOG [tick the correct box]   Needs more work ☐   Getting there ☐   Under control ☐

Themes: Separation and distance

QUICK QUESTION ✔

1 In which poem is the **theme** of **separation** absent? Why is this?

....

....

THINKING MORE DEEPLY ?

2 How does the regular **form** of each stanza suggest **separation** in 'Neutral Tones', and what **mood** does it help create?

....

....

....

....

3 Explain how both **distance** and **nearness** are explored in this quotation:

Quotation from 'Letters from Yorkshire': *'Still, it's you/who sends me word of that other world'* (11, 12)

Link to theme: ....

....

Effect: ....

....

4 Draw a line to match each of the quotations to the correct reason for separation. Then describe the **effect** below.

Quotation	Reason for separation
'They beckon to me from the other bank' (17)	end of the relationship
'Eden Rock'	growing apart
'I reach/towards a hatch that opens on an endless sky/to fall or fly' (13–15)	death
	disagreement
'Mother, any distance'	forced separation

Effect for 'Eden Rock': ....

....

Effect for 'Mother, any distance': ....

....

PROGRESS LOG [tick the correct box]   Needs more work ☐   Getting there ☐   Under control ☐

Themes: The natural world

1 Which of the **narrative** poems include rural settings? **Briefly** name or describe the settings.

a) ....

b) ....

THINKING MORE DEEPLY ?

2 How does **nature imagery** in the **last line** of 'Neutral Tones' convey the relationship between the speaker and the other person?

....

....

....

....

3 In the quotations below, identify the **techniques** used and describe their **effects**.

a) Quotation from 'Sonnet 29 "I think of thee!"': *'the straggling green'* (4)

Technique: ....

Effect: ....

....

....

....

> **TOP TIP** (A01)
>
> When focusing on nature imagery ask what feelings are evoked – joyful, gentle, bleak? Like all imagery it conveys the poem's mood and/or an aspect of something that prompts an emotion in the reader.

b) Quotation from 'Letters from Yorkshire': the associated meanings of *'lapwings return'* (2)

Technique: ....

....

Effect: ....

....

....

....

....

PROGRESS LOG [tick the correct box]   Needs more work ☐   Getting there ☐   Under control ☐

Themes: Death, time and memory

QUICK QUESTION ✔

1 In which poem does the speaker exist at a time before birth?

....

....

THINKING MORE DEEPLY ❓

2 How are **death**, **time** and **memory linked** and **conveyed** in 'Climbing My Grandfather'?

....

....

....

....

....

....

....

....

3 **Explain** how the quotations below relate to the **theme of death** and outline their **effects**.

a) Quotation from 'Porphyria's Lover': *'And all night long we have not stirred'* (59)

Link to theme of death: ....

....

Effect: ....

....

....

....

b) Quotation from 'The Farmer's Bride': *'On the black earth spread white with rime'* (38)

Link to theme of death: ....

....

Effect: ....

....

....

....

4 Find a quotation in the **first stanza** of 'Walking Away' that explores the **theme** of time, and complete the table.

Quotation	Effect

5 Find a quotation in the **last stanza** of 'When We Two Parted' that explores the **theme** of time, and complete the table.

Quotation	Effect

EXAM PREPARATION: COMPARING THEMES A02 ✏

6 Explain the importance of **memory** to the speakers in 'Neutral Tones' and 'Eden Rock'. Write **two paragraphs**. Make sure you include **two or more** quotations from each poem, and include the **effect** on the reader.

Use the space below for your first paragraph and then continue onto a separate sheet of paper.

....
....
....
....
....
....
....

> **TOP TIP** A02
>
> Remember, time is often linked to memory in the poems. However, it can be used in other ways. In 'Singh Song!' it is used to shift mood, so that the image, *'Late in di midnight hour'* (43) creates a sense of mystery.

PROGRESS LOG [tick the correct box]   Needs more work ☐   Getting there ☐   Under control ☐

Contexts: The Romantics and Victorians

1 Name a poem in the cluster that belongs to the **Romantic era** and another that is **Victorian**.

Romantic poem: ....

Victorian poem: ....

THINKING MORE DEEPLY **?**

2 Why do you think Shelley, as a poet of the Romantic period, drew on the **natural world** in 'Love's Philosophy' to express intense feelings?

....

....

....

3 Explain how the quotation below reveals **a feature of Romanticism**. Then describe the **effects** of the quotation.

Quotation from 'When We Two Parted': *'Long, long shall I rue thee'* (23)

Explanation: ....

....

Effect: ....

....

....

4 In what way does the **language** in 'The Farmer's Bride' suggest the poem was probably written in the **Victorian** period?

TOP TIP

The Romantic poets expressed intense personal emotions and often celebrated nature. While Victorian poets also expressed deep emotion, many focused on the social issues of the day such as poverty, or current and historical events.

....

....

....

....

....

....

PROGRESS LOG [tick the correct box]　Needs more work ☐　Getting there ☐　Under control ☐

Contexts: The Gothic

QUICK QUESTION ✔

1 When was the **Gothic narrative poem** fashionable?

....

....

THINKING MORE DEEPLY ?

2 Explain how the **setting** and **weather** in 'Porphyria's Lover' suit the **Gothic**.

....

....

....

....

3 Explain how the quotation below reveals features of the **Gothic**. Then describe the **effects** of the quotation.

Quotation from 'Porphyria's Lover': *'… her cheek once more/Blushed bright beneath my burning kiss'* **(47, 48)**

Explanation: ....

....

Effect: ....

....

4 Match the quotation from 'Porphyria's lover' to the correct feature. Then name the technique and explain its effect.

Quotation

'As a shut bud that holds a bee'
(43)

Features of the Gothic

secret places

crime, murder

the supernatural

extreme weather

> **TOP TIP** (A03)
>
> Remember, if a poem from the nineteenth century depicts the uncanny, such as the supernatural, secret places, ruins, strong feelings or disturbing events, it is probably influenced by the Gothic.

Technique: ....

....

Effect: ....

....

PROGRESS LOG [tick the correct box]   Needs more work ☐   Getting there ☐   Under control ☐

Contexts: The portrayal of women

QUICK QUESTION

1 Which poem with a modern setting challenges **stereotypical views** of women?

....

THINKING MORE DEEPLY

2 Where is the **setting** for 'Before You Were Mine', and what **mood** do these places create?

....

....

....

3 Describe what the quotations below reveal about different aspects of **women's lives,** and discuss the **context.**

a) Quotation from 'The Farmer's Bride': *'...I chose a maid,/Too young maybe'* (1, 2)

This reveals: ....

....

Context: ....

....

b) Quotation from 'Singh Song!': *'my bride/she hav a red crew cut'* (30, 31)

This reveals: ....

....

Context: ....

....

TOP TIP (A03)

Make sure you link the context to the poem in your responses: For example, in *'Sonnet 29 – "I think of thee!"'* the female speaker sees herself as her male lover's 'shadow', reflecting Victorian ideas about the role of women.

PROGRESS LOG [tick the correct box]   Needs more work ☐   Getting there ☐   Under control ☐

Practice task

1 First read this exam-style task:

> Compare how poets present attitudes to separation in 'Sonnet 29 – "I think of thee!"' and in one other poem from the cluster.

2 Begin by circling the **key words** in the **question** above.

3 Now complete this table, writing down three or four **points of comparison** with **evidence** and the **effect created**:

Point (poem 1)	Evidence/quotation and effect	Comparison (poem 2) evidence and effect

4 Draft your **response**. Use the space below for your first paragraph and then continue on a sheet of paper.

Start: *As the title and first line implies, the female speaker in 'Sonnet 29 – "I think of thee!"' is constantly thinking of the …*

....

....

....

....

....

....

....

....

....

....

....

PROGRESS LOG [tick the correct box]   Needs more work ☐   Getting there ☐   Under control ☐

PART FOUR: FORM, STRUCTURE AND LANGUAGE

Form and structure

1 Which of the poems in the cluster are **narrative poems**?

Poem 1: ....

Poem 2: ....

2 Which of the poems in the cluster are **lyric poems**?

Poem 1: ....

Poem 2: ....

3 How are the **stanzas** laid out in 'Letters from Yorkshire'?

....

....

4 Do you think 'Mother, any distance' is a **sonnet**? **Give evidence** for your answer, focusing on the **number of lines** in the poem.

Sonnets usually have ... .

....

....

....

....

However, 'Mother any Distance' differs from this by ... .

....

....

....

....

....

....

....

....

5 Complete the table below by deciding on the **form** of each poem, and how the form suits its **meaning**.

Poem	Form	Suits meaning because ...
'Climbing My Grandfather'		
'Singh Song!'		

6 How does the **first line** of 'Climbing My Grandfather' suggest **danger**, and what does it mean for the speaker?

....

....

....

....

....

7 Why is stanza five a **turning point** in 'The Farmer's Bride'? What is the **effect**?

....

....

....

....

....

8 Why do you think 'Singh Song!' ends with **couplets**? What **mood** does this convey?

....

....

....

....

....

9 How does the **form** of 'Winter Swans' differ in the **final stanza**, and why do you think this is?

....

....

....

....

....

10 Why do you think the **last line** of 'Eden Rock' is set apart?

> **TOP TIP** (A02)
>
> If the verse form in a poem changes, it will create an effect. For example, in 'Mother, any distance', the final stanza is no longer a quatrain. It reflects the unreeling tape measure and the tension between mother and son.

....

....

....

....

....

....

....

....

....

....

EXAM PREPARATION: WRITING ABOUT POETIC FORM AND STRUCTURE (A02) ✐

11 Explain the form and structure of 'Porphyria's Lover'. Use the space below for your first paragraph and then continue onto a separate piece of paper. Make sure you include **two** quotations and discuss the **effects** on the reader.

....

....

....

....

....

....

....

....

....

....

....

PROGRESS LOG [tick the correct box]   Needs more work ☐   Getting there ☐   Under control ☐

Rhyme, rhythm and sound

1 What is the **rhyme scheme** of the **first stanza** of 'The Farmer's Bride'?

....

....

2 What kind of **rhyme** is found in 'Walking Away', and **where** does it occur?

....

....

3 Describe the **rhythm** of 'When We Two Parted', considering what it reminds you of and why it suits the poem.

....

....

....

....

....

....

....

....

4 'Porphyria's Lover' is written in **iambic pentameter**. What does this mean, and why does it suit the poem?

....

....

....

....

....

....

....

....

5 Complete the table below by finding examples of the stated **technique** in the poems, and describing their **effects**.

Technique	Example/reference	Effect
Caesura in *'The Farmer's Bride' (44)*		
Enjambment in *'Love's Philosophy' (the first octave)*		

EXAM PREPARATION: WRITING ABOUT RHYTHM (A02) ✏

6 Read what a student has written about the enjambment used in 'Sonnet 29 – "I think of thee!"' Then finish the second **sentence** by describing another **example** and the **effect** of enjambment in the poem.

Enjambment is often used in 'Sonnet 29 – "I think of thee!"'. It helps the voice to flow so that, for example, the run-on line from 1 to 2 makes the voice seem natural.

It also … ....

....

....

PROGRESS LOG [tick the correct box]   Needs more work ☐   Getting there ☐   Under control ☐

Voice and viewpoint

QUICK QUESTION ✔

1 From whose **viewpoint** is 'Follower' written?

....

....

THINKING MORE DEEPLY ?

2 Which poem in particular has a **voice** the **reader** would **not trust**? Say why, and explain the **effect** created by this.

....

....

....

....

3 In 'When We Two Parted', who does the speaker **address** and what **mood** is conveyed?

....

....

....

....

EXAM PREPARATION: WRITING ABOUT VIEWPOINT A02 ✎

4 Read what a student has written about the viewpoint used in 'Letters from Yorkshire'. Then, on a separate piece of paper, add a further **sentence** describing the **effect** created by the change in viewpoint.

In 'Letters from Yorkshire' the viewpoint changes. At first the speaker is talking to the reader, telling us about her friend and what 'he' is doing. However in stanza two the viewpoint shifts and the speaker addresses the friend in the second person, 'You'.

....

....

....

....

PROGRESS LOG [tick the correct box]   Needs more work ☐   Getting there ☐   Under control ☐

Imagery

QUICK QUESTIONS ✔

1 What kind of **imagery** is used in 'Winter Swans'?

....

....

2 Which of the poems uses **religious imagery**?

....

....

THINKING MORE DEEPLY ?

3 What **image** of the **speaker's appearance** do we have in **stanza three** of 'Singh Song!', and what does it tell us about him?

....

....

....

....

....

....

....

....

....

....

....

4 In the quotation below identify the **technique** used, explain its **effect** and say what **theme** it is linked to.

Quotation from 'Walking Away': *'with leaves just turning'* (2)

Technique: ....

....

Effect: ....

....

Theme: ....

....

5 Complete the table below by identifying each of the **techniques** and explaining their **effects**.

Quotation	Technique	Effect
'Straight and slight as a young larch tree' (31) 'The Farmer's Bride'		
'di brightey moon' (50) 'Singh Song!'		

EXAM PREPARATION: WRITING ABOUT IMAGERY (A02)

6 Read what a student has written about an image used in 'The Farmer's Bride'. Then, on a separate piece of paper, add a **sentence** describing the **effect** created by the image.

When the young wife in 'The Farmer's Bride' is caught after trying to escape from

her husband she is 'All in a shiver and a scare'. ....

....

....

....

PROGRESS LOG [tick the correct box]   Needs more work ☐   Getting there ☐   Under control ☐

Poetic devices

QUICK QUESTIONS ✓

1 What **theme** is illustrated by the **pathetic fallacy** *'the waves clasp one another'* (10) from 'Love's Philosophy'?

....

....

2 Find a **quotation** in the third stanza of 'Letters from Yorkshire' that is **ambiguous**.

....

....

THINKING MORE DEEPLY ?

3 Explain how **irony** is used in 'Porphyria's Lover'.

The poem opens with the description of ... .

....

....

....

This is contrasted with ... .

....

....

....

....

4 What kind of question is used as a **technique** in 'When We Two Parted'? Name the technique and its **purpose**, and give an **example**.

....

....

....

....

....

....

....

....

5 Complete the table by finding an example of the **technique** given, and/or describing its **effect**.

Technique	Quotation/example	Effect
Pathetic fallacy/ personification (*'Neutral Tones'* first stanza)		*Gives the earth or soil human qualities, emphasising how the relationship is dying from the lack of emotional nourishment or love.*
Image (*'Before You Were Mine'*)	*'where you sparkle and waltz and laugh before you were mine'*	

EXAM PREPARATION: WRITING ABOUT POETIC TECHNIQUES

6 Read what a student has written about a technique used in 'Climbing My Grandfather'. Then, on a separate piece of paper, add **a sentence** describing the effect of the **oxymoron**.

In 'Climbing My Grandfather' the poet chooses a simile to show how the skin of the grandfather's finger is 'like warm ice'. However the poet also uses another

technique at the same time, called an oxymoron. ....

....

....

TOP TIP (A01)

Not all language will be a specific technique or device. In the exam you can refer to the specific word choices the poet makes, particularly if you want to describe the use of an important line or moment in the poem.

PROGRESS LOG [tick the correct box]   Needs more work ☐   Getting there ☐   Under control ☐

Tone and mood

1 Think of a **word or phrase** that sums up the **mood** of 'Love's Philosophy'.

....

....

THINKING MORE DEEPLY ❓

2 What **mood** is conveyed by the final lines of 'Walking Away': *'How selfhood begins with a walking away,/And love is proved in the letting go'*?

....

....

....

3 Explain how the quotation below suggests the **mood**, and describe its **effect**.

Quotation from 'Singh Song!': *'she effing at my mum/in all di colours of Punjabi'* (23, 24)

Mood: ....

....

Effect: ....

....

EXAM PREPARATION: WRITING ABOUT MOOD (A02) ✏

4 **Explain** what **mood** is conjured up in the image *'icebergs of white feather'* (11) in 'Winter Swans'.

....

....

....

....

....

....

PROGRESS LOG [tick the correct box]   Needs more work ☐   Getting there ☐   Under control ☐

Practice task

1 First read this exam-style task:

> Compare how poets use the ending of their poems to present relationships in 'When We Two Parted' and in one other poem from the cluster.

2 Begin by circling the **key words** in the **question** above.

3 Now complete this table, writing down three or four **points of comparison** with **evidence** and the **effect created**:

Point (poem 1)	Evidence/quotation and effect	Comparison (poem 2) evidence and effect

4 Draft your **response**. Use the space below for your first paragraph and then continue on a sheet of paper.

Start: *The ending of 'When We Two Parted' confirms the deep sorrow the speaker feels will never ...*

....

....

....

....

....

....

....

....

....

....

....

....

PROGRESS LOG [tick the correct box]   Needs more work ☐   Getting there ☐   Under control ☐

PART FIVE: COMPARING POEMS

Evaluating poems

STARTING TO COMPARE

1 Read what a student has written about the ideas presented in 'Eden Rock' and 'Winter Swans'.

The rural setting in 'Winter Swans' portrays a gloomy picture of a landscape overwhelmed by 'two days' of rain. Everything seems drenched as the couple walk around the lake. In contrast, many of the images in 'Eden Rock' evoke a summer day from a memory of childhood. The mother wears a 'sprigged' dress that suggests summer flowers. The focus on so much bleak rain in 'Winter Swans' has connotations of tears. The opposite occurs in 'Eden Rock'. A sense of heat is created through the way 'The sky whitens', reminding us of the way your eyes can be dazzled by the sun on a very hot day.

2 What is the theme being compared in the paragraph? Choose from the list of themes by circling the most suitable one.

Weather		The natural world
Love	Memory	Separation

3 What else could have been mentioned about the theme in each poem? Write another paragraph underneath.

....

....

....

....

....

....

....

TOP TIP (A01)

Remember, a theme will run through the whole poem. When you are asked to compare two poems, make sure you recognise what the main theme is and keep it in mind as you answer the question.

....

....

....

....

....

....

....

Using connectives

1 Read what a student has written about the context of 'The Farmer's Bride' and 'Sonnet 29 – "I think of thee!".

The young wife in 'The Farmer's Bride' does not conform to the Victorian idea of what a wife is supposed to be. .... she does her domestic duties as expected, she tries her best to avoid relations with her husband. She is seen as odd, as if she was 'not a woman'. .... her extreme fear of 'men-folk' in general suggests former abuse that has not been recognised. .... she has no power there is little she can do. ...., the only way she can act is to try and escape. .... the speaker in 'Sonnet 29 – "I think of thee!"' fits the idea of what a Victorian woman should be. She is like the clinging 'vine' who exists 'within' her lover's 'shadow'. .... and to reinforce the difference, the male lover is described as the strong 'palm-tree'.

Complete this gap-fill paragraph with the most suitable connectives from the box below. You will need to make the first letter of the connective a capital if it starts a sentence.

in addition	too	in contrast
since	later	although
instead	however	likewise

2 Use connectives to write another paragraph contrasting the way the modern bride in 'Singh Song!' behaves.

....

....

....

....

....

....

....

....

....

....

Using quotations

1 Read what a student has written, comparing 'Follower' with 'Before You Were Mine', in which the quotations have been left out.

The speaker in 'Follower' looks back at his childhood and recalls his father

working the .... He remembers how his father turned

the earth over .... it, a perfect action that reveals what

.... his father was. Unlike the rural setting in 'Follower',

'Before You Were Mine' has an urban setting. Here the speaker imagines

a time .... before she was born. In her imagination she

sees her mother as a young glamorous woman in a .... or

making her way across .... in Glasgow.

Write the quotations below in the correct gaps above.

'An expert'	'ten years'	'horse-plough'
'George Square'	'without breaking'	'polka-dot dress'

2 Using the following quotations from different poems, fit them neatly into separate sentences and show their effect.

> *'dripping cloak and shawl'* (11) from 'Porphyria's Lover'
>
> *'on an endless sky'* (14) from 'Mother, any distance'
>
> *'If thou kiss not me?'* (16) from 'Love's Philosophy'

Porphyria arrives at the cottage ... .

....

....

....

....

....

At the end of the poem the speaker ... .

....

....

A rhetorical question ... .

....

....

TOP TIP (A01)

Do not make your quotations too long, and remember you can split a quotation to fit into a sentence, as in this example about 'Walking Away': It is the end of summer when the *'leaves'* are *'just turning'*.

Writing a comparison

1 First read the following exam-style question. Underline the most important words for answering this question effectively. You should keep the key words in mind when you write your paragraph in Question 2.

> Compare how poets present ideas about betrayal in relationships in 'When We Two Parted' and 'Neutral Tones'.

2 Now write your own paragraph comparing the two poems. Use the following writing prompts to organise your paragraph:

Start with a general topic sentence beginning: *'Both ...'*

Continue with a sentence explaining one similarity: *'For example, in ...'*

Continue with a sentence explaining how this links to the second poem: *'In the same way ...'*

Finish with a rounding-off sentence: *'So ...'*

Continue on a separate piece of paper if you need to. Remember to include one or two quotations.

Both ... .

....

....

For example, in ... .

....

....

....

....

In the same way ... .

....

....

....

....

So ... .

....

....

....

PROGRESS LOG [tick the correct box]   Needs more work ☐   Getting there ☐   Under control ☐

Practice task

1 First read this exam-style task:

> Compare how the poets present attitudes to family ties in 'Climbing My Grandfather' and one other poem from the cluster.

2 Begin by circling the **key words** in the **question** above.

3 Now complete this table, writing down three or four **points of comparison** with **evidence** and the **effect created**:

Point (poem 1)	Evidence/quotation and effect	Comparison (poem 2) evidence and effect

4 Draft your **response**. Use the space below for your first paragraph and then continue on a sheet of paper.

Start: *The speaker in 'Climbing My Grandfather' makes a journey in an attempt to get closer to …*

....

....

....

....

....

....

....

....

....

....

....

PROGRESS LOG [tick the correct box] Needs more work ☐ Getting there ☐ Under control ☐

PART SIX: PROGRESS BOOSTER

Key skills and using quotations

1 How well can you express your ideas about the poems from the cluster? Look at this grid and tick the level you think you are currently at:

Level	How you respond	Tick
High to Very High	• You select quotations and references very precisely and you embed them fluently in your sentences. • You analyse and explore the poets' methods and effects with detailed insight, and a thorough knowledge of poetic terminology. • You are convincing with your ideas, and offer different interpretations and perspectives. • You compare poems in a detailed and very structured way, moving fluently between ideas in the two poems.	
Mid	• You support what you say with evidence and quotations. • You explain writers' methods and effects clearly, using appropriate terminology. • You show clear understanding of the main ideas and make some links between ideas. • You compare poems clearly and support your links between them.	
Lower	• You sometimes use quotations to back up what you say, but they are not always well chosen, nor fluently embedded in the text. • You comment on some methods and effects, but not always using the correct terminology. • You show some basic understanding of ideas, but these tend to be undeveloped. • You make some basic comparisons between the poems.	

SELECTING AND USING QUOTATIONS

2 Read these two samples from students' responses to a question about separation in 'Walking Away'. Decide which of the three levels they fit best, i.e. **lower** (L), **mid** (M) or **high** (H).

Student A: *The father describes the moment when his son walks away towards his new school saying that he is only 'half-fledged'. It suggests he is like a baby bird. So we learn that the boy must be very young to be away from his parents. This must be very hard for parents when it happens.*

Level? ☐   Why? ....

....

....

Student B: *The poet creates a powerful metaphor when the speaker describes his son walking away to attend his new boarding school. The child is only 'a half-fledged thing' suggesting that, like a young bird not fully grown, he is too young to leave the security of home. The image of the bird's helplessness also evokes a mood of sadness so that we sense the father's sorrow at losing his son.*

Level? ☐   Why? ....

....

....

❸ Which of the following quotations from the poem 'Walking Away' would be suitable if you were exploring the theme of memory?

   a) Quotation 1: *'Like a winged seed loosened from its parent stem'* (12)

   b) Quotation 2: *'It is eighteen years ago, almost to the day –'* (1)

   c) Quotation 3: *'… the gait of one/Who finds no path where the path should be'* (9, 10)

❹ Write a sentence explaining why:

   ....

   ....

❺ Here is the first part of another student response, which includes a quotation from 'Walking Away'. Complete the response by explaining what the quotation reveals, or its effect.

   The speaker describes how 'the small, the scorching/ordeals' that we suffer in life

   may not seem that important, but … ....

   ....

   ....

⸻

USING QUOTATIONS TO COMPARE

❻ Here are two quotations from different poems about contrasting relationships.

   Quotation 1: *'I've hardly heard her speak at all'* (29) 'The Farmer's Bride'

   Quotation 2: *'thoughts do twine and bud'* (1) 'Sonnet 29 – "I think of thee!"'

   Complete this paragraph, using the quotations to make a comparison, and embedding them fluently:

   When the farmer states .... *it suggests/*

   conveys the idea that ....

   However, in 'Sonnet 29 – "I think of thee!"' ....

   ....

⸻

PROGRESS LOG [tick the correct box]   Needs more work ☐   Getting there ☐   Under control ☐

Using structure and paragraphs effectively

Paragraphs need to demonstrate your points clearly by:

- using **topic sentences**
- focusing on **key words** from quotations
- explaining their **effect** or meaning.

1 Read this model paragraph in which a student explains how Charlotte Mew presents the farmer in 'The Farmer's Bride'.

> *Mew presents the character of the farmer partly through voice and dialect. When he complains that there's more 'to do/At harvest-time than bide and woo' we gain a strong sense of his rural voice. More importantly, the dismissive way he uses the verbs 'bide' and 'woo', meaning giving time to courtship, suggests that for him, as a hard-working farmer, marriage is more of a contract than about love.*

Look at the response carefully.

- **Underline** the topic sentence that explains the main point about the farmer.
- **Circle** the words that are picked out from the quotation.
- **Highlight** or put a tick next to the part of the last sentence that explains the words.

2 Now read this paragraph by a student who is explaining how Mew presents the farmer's wife:

> *She is a very young and nervous bride who is afraid of men and loves animals. When she runs away we are told that the she is 'flying like a hare', so we know she wants to escape badly.*

Expert viewpoint: This paragraph is unclear. It does not begin with a topic sentence to explain how Mew presents the wife and doesn't zoom in on any key words to analyse what the wife is like or explain effects.

Now **rewrite the paragraph**. Start with a **topic sentence**, and pick out a **key word or phrase** to **'zoom in'** on, then follow up with an explanation or interpretation, including any effect created.

Mew presents the farmer's wife … ....

....

....

....

....

....

....

LINKING IDEAS WITHIN A POEM

It is equally important to show that your ideas are fully developed by referring to different parts of a poem.

❸ Read this model paragraph by one student writing about the relationship between mother and son in 'Mother, any distance'.

> *Armitage presents the son's attempts to break away from his mother's control in stanza one through images that portray freedom. For example, 'prairies' in the 'prairies of the floors' implies wide open spaces. This contrasts with the confined space of a house interior. In addition, another image of space occurs at the very end of the poem when the son opens the hatch in the loft on to 'an endless sky'. Here it suggests unlimited space and again the idea of freedom – a freedom that is available if the son wishes to take it.*

Look at the response carefully.

- **Underline** the topic sentence which introduces the main idea.
- **Circle** the first quotation used.
- **Highlight** the sentence that signals a change in ideas or link to another part of the poem.
- **Tick** any words or phrases that show these links in ideas, such as 'who', 'when', 'implying', 'which', etc.

❹ Read this paragraph by another student about the nature of romantic love in 'Love's Philosophy'.

> *The poet says that everything in nature has a partner or combines with something else. The speaker says, for example, that fountains flow into rivers. He also says that rivers flow into oceans. He uses the word 'mingle', which means this and has a soft sound. So it makes it seem a pleasant thing.*

Expert viewpoint: The candidate has shown some understanding of the main idea in 'Love's Philosophy'. However, the paragraph is rather awkwardly written. It needs improving by linking the sentences with suitable phrases and joining words, such as 'where', 'in', 'as well as', 'who', 'suggesting' and 'implying'. It also needs a further linking point added at the end to another part of the poem.

Rewrite the **paragraph**, improving the **style**, and also try to add a **further sentence** which links to another part of the poem or aspect.

Start with the same **topic sentence**, but extend it:

The poet says that everything in nature … ....

....

....

Making inferences and interpretations

WRITING ABOUT INFERENCES

You need to be able to show you can read between the lines, and make inferences, rather than just explain more explicit 'surface' meanings.

1 Read this paragraph about **images** from the poem 'Before You Were Mine'.

> *The speaker imagines that before she was born, her mother's life in the city as a young woman was glamorous and thrilling. The vibrant nightlife is conjured up through the image of 'the ballroom with the thousand eyes', which we can assume is the glitter ball in the centre of the room. However through connotations of light, the image also suggests the light in the dancers' eyes and makes associations with the bright lights of the city and youthful excitement.*

- **Underline** the topic sentence that introduces the main idea.
- **Circle** the sentence that develops the first point.
- **Highlight** the sentence that shows inference and begins to explore wider interpretation.

2 Here is a line from the poem 'Before You Were Mine': *'till I see you, clear as scent, under the tree,/with its lights'* (14, 15).

Which one of the following is an **inference** you could draw from the line?

a) The image suggests the speaker's mother as she waits beside a tree.

b) The image suggests the smell of perfume in the air and lights on a tree.

c) The image suggests the speaker's intense love for her mother.

Why? Write a sentence explaining why this is an appropriate inference.

....

....

INTERPRETING – YOUR TURN!

3 Now write your own paragraph, continuing on separate paper, about the character of Porphyria from 'Porphyria's Lover' in which you make inferences and explore wider interpretations.

In 'Porphyria's Lover' ... .

....

....

....

PROGRESS LOG [tick the correct box]   Needs more work ☐   Getting there ☐   Under control ☐

Writing about context

EXPLAINING CONTEXT

When you write about context you must make sure that what you write is relevant to the task.

Read this comment by a student about challenging stereotypes in 'Singh Song!':

> *The speaker's bride is very independent, doing what she wants and dressing as she pleases. She wears a combination of styles, such as a 'Tartan sari', builder's jacket and a 'red' punk-style 'crew cut'. Her choices suggest a multicultural Britain, rather than the stereotypical view that all Sikh wives wear particular kinds of clothes.*

❶ Underline the contextual point made in the paragraph.

YOUR TURN!

❷ Now read this further paragraph, and complete it by choosing a suitable point related to context, selecting from a), b) or c) below.

> *The speaker runs one of his father's grocer's shops, but shows no real interest in the business. He regularly locks the shop when there are no customers and goes upstairs to make love to his new wife. His neglect of the business, shown in the line …*

a) *'Late in di midnight hour … ven di precinct is concrete-cool' creates an image of the urban environment at night, suggesting that the day has been hot with romantic passion.*

b) *'in di worst Indian shop/on di whole Indian road –' reveals the speaker's lack of interest in making money and challenges the stereotype of the Asian shopkeeper.*

c) *'she effing at my mum/in all di colours of Punjabi' compares the wife's vivid swearing with the vivid colours of the Punjab.*

❸ Now write a short paragraph about the title of the poem and how the poet uses it to challenge the stereotype sometimes given to English/Punjabi speakers.

....

....

....

....

....

....

PROGRESS LOG [tick the correct box]   Needs more work ☐   Getting there ☐   Under control ☐

Tackling exam tasks

DECODING QUESTIONS

It is important to be able to identify **key words** in exam tasks and then quickly generate some ideas.

1 a) Read this task and notice how the **key words** have been underlined.

Question: <u>Compare</u> how writers <u>present ideas</u> about <u>family ties</u> in <u>'Eden Rock'</u> and <u>one other poem</u> in the cluster.

b) Now do the same with this task, i.e. underline the key words:

Question: Compare how writers present ideas about separation in 'The Farmer's Bride' and one other poem from the cluster.

GENERATING IDEAS

2 Now, in response to the question above, you need to generate ideas quickly. Remember, you are discussing **two poems**. Use the spider diagrams* below and add as many ideas of your own as you can:

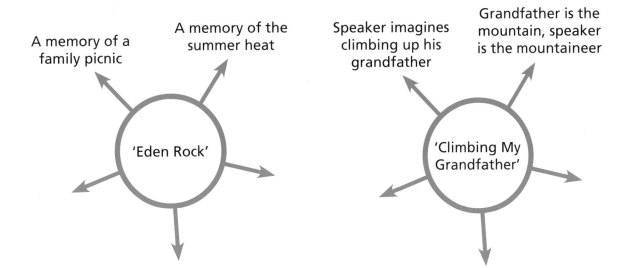

A memory of a family picnic

A memory of the summer heat

'Eden Rock'

Speaker imagines climbing up his grandfather

Grandfather is the mountain, speaker is the mountaineer

'Climbing My Grandfather'

*You can do these as lists if you wish.

PLANNING AN ESSAY

3 **Using the ideas you generated** above, write a simple **plan** with **four key points on the first poem, and four points on the second** (the first two have been done for you on page 76).

Check back to your spider diagrams or the lists you made. This structure deals with the poems in two halves of the essay (but alternatively, if you prefer, you could link and contrast points a), points b), etc. as you write the essay, moving from one poem to the other and back again).

Introduction: Brief recap of 'story' of poems and focus of task	
First half of essay: 'Eden Rock'	**Second half of essay: 'Climbing My Grandfather'**
a) The speaker recalls a family picnic when he was a boy.	a) The speaker imagines climbing up his grandfather from his feet to his head.
b) He describes the picnic and the summer heat.	b) The grandfather is like a mountain, the speaker a mountaineer.
c)	c) ....
d)	d) ....
Conclusion:	

❹ Now list at least **four quotations** for each poem (these can be single words or phrases), one for each point from the table above (the first two have been provided for you):

First poem: 'Eden Rock'. Quotations I could use for a), b), c), d)	**Comparison poem: 'Climbing My Grandfather'. Quotations I could use for a), b), c), d)**
a) 'They are waiting for me somewhere beyond Eden Rock'	a) 'I decide to do it free without a rope or net'
b) 'The sky whitens as if lit by three suns'	b) 'for climbing has its dangers'
c)	c) ....
d)	d) ....

❺ Now read this task and **write a plan of your own**, including **quotations**, on a separate sheet of paper.

Question: Compare how writers present ideas about separation in 'When We Two Parted' and one other poem in the anthology.

PROGRESS LOG [tick the correct box]   Needs more work ☐   Getting there ☐   Under control ☐

Sample answers

OPENING PARAGRAPHS

Here is the task from the previous page:

Question: Compare how writers present ideas about family ties in 'Eden Rock' and one other poem in the cluster.

Now look at these two alternative openings to the essay.

Student A

> *In both poems the speakers are looking back to childhood. In Causley's poem, told in the present tense, the speaker imagines a family picnic, in which his parents are 'waiting' for him 'beyond Eden Rock'. 'Eden', suggests the Garden of Eden, a symbol of Paradise. In Waterhouse's poem the speaker, a grandson is trying to get close to his grandfather and decides to climb up him, like a child might do. The grandfather seems to be the mountain and the speaker the mountaineer.*

Student B

> *In 'Eden Rock' the speaker seems to be remembering when he was a child and a special time he had. It is a family picnic he had as a boy with his mother and father and the dog. The picnic takes place near a stream and place called Eden Rock. It is a sunny day. In 'Climbing My Grandfather' the speaker decides he is going to climb up his grandfather. Although this sounds a strange thing to do, it is because he is thinking of his grandfather as if he was a mountain. The thing that both poems have in common is that the speakers seem to be looking back to childhood.*

A good opening paragraph will:

- briefly and concisely introduce the 'story' of the two poems and how they interrelate
- relate the poems to the focus of the task
- if space, include brief quotations to help 'set the scene' for the essay.

1 Which of these two openings does this (circle one)? A or B

2 Mark or annotate the skills shown in the better opening paragraph (for example, concise reference to the 'story' of the poem).

3 Now it's your turn. Write the opening paragraph to this task on a separate sheet of paper.

Question: Compare how writers present ideas about youth and age in a relationship in 'Follower' and one other poem in the cluster.

Remember:

- Introduce the topic in general terms, concisely mentioning the poems' stories.
- **Explain** or **'unpick'** the key **words** or **ideas** in the task (such as the theme or key idea mentioned).
- Include at least one brief quotation (from at least one poem) relating to the focus.
- Use the **poets' names**.

You could start: *In 'Follower' Heaney presents a striking picture of the father as a ploughman, in which the speaker recalls his memories of …*

BODY PARAGRAPHS

Here are two main paragraphs in response to the same task above. These focus on the techniques used by the poet, and their effects.

Student A

In 'Eden Rock' it is summer when the parents are having the picnic. We can tell this because the mother is wearing a 'sprigged dress', which means that it is flowery. She also wears a 'straw hat', so it must be a very warm day. The title 'Eden Rock' reminds us of the Garden of Eden. In the Christian religion this is Paradise. So the poet is giving us a picture of Paradise.

Student B

The imagery in 'Eden Rock' emphasises the summer season and rural setting. The speaker's mother wears a 'sprigged dress', and a 'straw hat'. The images remind us of summer flowers, gardens and warm days with links to Eden, as the ideal garden in Christianity and other religions. Later in the poem, connections with the other-worldly image of the 'three suns' are also suggested. Not only does it emphasise summer heat, but also the deep warmth the speaker feels for his parents. In addition 'three suns' has connotations of the Christian trinity, holy family and the speaker's family, reinforcing the idea that the speaker is seeing his parents in Paradise.

4 Look again at the grid for High, Mid and Low responses on page 69.

What level seems to match each student's response?

Student A: ....

Why? ....

Student B: ....

Why? ....

5 Now, take another **aspect** of either poem 1 or poem 2 and write your own **paragraph**. You could **comment** on one of these aspects:

● The speaker's attitude or preparations at the beginning of the poem

● How the form and structure affects the poem's meaning

● The end of the poem

....

....

....

....

....

....

....

CONCLUDING PARAGRAPHS

Your final paragraph should:

- round off or concisely **sum up** any overall view or perspective
- touch on, or hint at, the **differences** between poems as well as the links
- efficiently **recap** ideas without listing them again (perhaps ending with a quotation you haven't used before)

Here is an effective final paragraph comparing ideas around fathers and sons in 'Follower' and 'Walking Away':

> Both poems, then, explore the ties that bind father and son, but which are inevitably broken as time progresses. As 'Walking Away' suggests, by letting your child go, you give them freedom and self-determination, but as 'Follower' suggests, that freedom might involve difficult or guilty choices on the part of the child too. The different perspectives (the son as narrator in 'Follower' and the father as narrator in 'Walking Away') both reveal this pain of letting go through the act of walking – as the child leaves the waiting father behind at the school gates, or watches the father 'stumbling' in his tracks.

6 Now complete these tasks:

- **Underline** any sentences that provide a general summing-up of both poems.
- **Circle** any points that suggest the differences in the two poems.
- **Highlight** the final 'recap' sentence, which cleverly links the two poems.
- **Tick** the final quotation used.

7 Practise writing concluding paragraphs of your own, using the same techniques.

COMPARING THE POEMS

Read the following longer extract in response to the task on page 78.

Response A

> 'Eden Rock' is a poem written by Charles Causley and the speaker of the poem is thinking about when he was a child and the family had a picnic. We know this because there is a picnic tablecloth spread out on the grass and there is tea from a Thermos flask. The speaker in the poem is on the other side of the stream and is trying to get across to his parents. They are telling him to go the easy way.
>
> 'Climbing My Grandfather' is by Andrew Waterhouse and in it the speaker pretends he is climbing up his grandfather. He starts with his grandfather's shoes and then gets to his waist and then his arm and so on. It seems to be hard work and it says he has a rest. He feels relieved and happy when he gets to the top

8 Write down three things to change or develop in this response.

a) ....

b) ....

c) ....

9 Rewrite the paragraph on a separate piece of paper, making the changes you think are needed.

Now read this second response to the task on page 78.

Response B

'Eden Rock' is concerned with looking at the links that we still have with our parents after they are dead. The speaker imagines what it would be like to be with his parents again when he himself is dying and is 'Crossing' 'the stream-path'. The image could refer to crossing over to the afterlife. He has a picture in his mind of the family he knew when he was a child growing up and his parents were young. It is happy picture and he seems to want to get back to that.

'Climbing My Grandfather' is also concerned with family ties, but in this poem the speaker wants to get close to his grandfather. Examples of the grandfather's clothes are given as the speaker climbs him. He has 'old brogues, dusty and cracked', so perhaps he didn't care much about his appearance. But later the poet gives us an image of his 'earth-stained' hands, which tells us why. He probably worked on the land. Like the parents in 'Eden Rock' we get the impression that the grandfather is dead and also that the speakers in both poems want to regain a closeness to their relatives and to their own childhoods.

10 In what ways is this response better than Response A on page 79? List three aspects:

a) ....

b) ....

c) ....

11 Look again at the criteria table on page 69. What else would the student need to do to improve it even more?

....

....

....

....

....

....

12 Write your own version of the response below:

....

....

....

....

....

....

....

EVALUATING A RESPONSE

Read this sample response to the following task:

Question: Compare how poets present attitudes to the breakdown between people in 'Winter Swans' and one other poem in the anthology.

In both 'Winter Swans' and 'Neutral Tones' the poets have chosen a first person perspective and both speakers are recalling an event while also addressing their lovers or partners. In 'Winter Swans' the speaker and his lover circle a lake 'silent and apart', suggesting a rift between them. In Thomas Hardy's 'Neutral Tones' the setting is similar. The poem opens as the speaker recalls a memory in which he and the other person stood by a pond one bleak winter day.

In 'Winter Swans' heavy rain has meant the earth is saturated. It is described as 'gulping for breath'. The image is a pathetic fallacy, and 'gulping' in particular with its throaty sound suggests the struggle to survive. This in turn implies that the relationship is struggling to survive, so the reader can infer that the rift between the couple has been extreme. We can also deduce that the couple's silence means there has been a pause in the quarrel, emphasised by a dash or pause at the end of the first line. In 'Neutral Tones' there has also been a breakdown in the relationship, but in this poem the breakdown seems more severe. The speaker feels desolate. He regards the smile of the person, whom he must have loved once, as 'the deadest thing', emphasising a sense of hopelessness. The speaker feels betrayed by love. The use of the sibilant in the word 'deceives' creates a hissing, snake-like sound, suggesting slyness. The feelings the speaker expresses become harsher when the lover's 'grin of bitterness' is described using the simile 'like an ominous bird a-wing'. For most readers this simile would have a powerful effect with connotations of cruelty or ill will, which seems to be totally absent from 'Winter Swans'.

In both poems nature imagery is key. However, the images of the landscape in 'Neutral Tones' constantly suggest a lifeless world that heightens the sense we have of the dead relationship. For example, the tree by the pond is an 'ash' tree, which has a double meaning. As well as being a tree, 'ash' can refer to the remains of a fire or even to a cremated body. The title of the poem also reinforces the picture of a colourless world. Although the setting is also bleak in 'Winter Swans', the weather has been stormy rather than lifeless. Perhaps this implies that unlike the relationship in Hardy's poem, passion is still present, and therefore there is hope for the relationship. As we read on in 'Winter Swans' we realise that the example of the swans, who 'mate for life', and who act 'in unison' is the means by which the two lovers are reconciled. In addition, the swans are portrayed as 'porcelain' and their whiteness conveys the idea of marriage and unity, unlike the white sun of Neutral Tones, which seems bleached, as though it is lifeless. There seems to be no possibility of reconciliation in 'Neutral Tones' as there is in 'Winter Swans' and both these features are shown by the form and structure of the poems.

Each poem has a repetitive verse pattern. 'Winter Swans' is mostly made up of tercets, and these move easily from one stanza to the next (suggesting the continuing walk around the lake). 'Neutral Tones' has four regular quatrains, but unlike the former poem, the last line of each quatrain is set apart as though the stanza has faltered, just as the relationship has. The rhythm of a single line in stanza three also judders and does not read well. This helps to accentuate the sense the reader has of the broken relationship.

Finally, at the very end of both poems, we can see how the different structures sum up the state of each relationship. In 'Neutral Tones' the last line reminds us of the first one, by referring again to the pond and the dead leaves. The structure is circular. This implies that the relationship cannot change or improve. In addition the viewpoint has shifted in the final stanza to the present tense, confirming the lack of improvement over time. In contrast, 'Winter Swans' finishes on a hopeful note with a couplet, often used in love poems. The quarrel is resolved as the two lovers are reunited by holding hands.

Your task:

🔞 Highlight **successful aspects** of this response. For example, **underline** or **circle**:

- Examples of relevant points made
- Any points of comparison
- Clear use of paragraphs to move between the poems
- Relevant and fluent use of quotations
- Any deeper or more detailed interpretations
- Good overall structure – opening paragraph, main paragraphs, concluding paragraphs
- Relevant reference to poetic language and devices
- Relevant reference to form and structure
- Relevant reference to effects created by language, form and structure

Then, check the grid on page 69 and decide what the right level is for the response. Finally, check the answer to see if you are correct.

Further questions

Write **full-length responses** to the following exam-style questions:

1. Compare how the poets present attitudes towards being apart in 'Letters from Yorkshire' and one other poem from the cluster.

2. Compare how the poets present attitudes towards a family member in 'Before You Were Mine' and one other poem from the cluster.

3. Compare how the poets present attitudes towards marriage or partnerships in 'Love's Philosophy' and one other poem from the cluster.

4. Compare how the poets present attitudes towards a parent in 'Mother, any distance' and one other poem from the cluster.

5. Compare how poets present attitudes towards romantic love in 'Sonnet 29 – "I think of thee!"' and one other poem from the cluster.

PROGRESS LOG [tick the correct box]   Needs more work ☐   Getting there ☐   Under control ☐

ANSWERS

Note: Answers have been provided for most tasks. Exceptions are 'Practice tasks'.

PART TWO: EXPLORING THE POEMS [PP. 8–38]

When We Two Parted [pp. 8–9]

1 The title and first line tell the reader the poem will be about the break-up of a relationship.

2 Word: 'sever' (4). Effect: the verb suggests a final, brutal separation. (There is also a word association with 'sever' and 'ever', suggesting finality.)

3 Stanza three includes the metaphor 'A knell in mine ear' (18), which refers to the 'knell' sound of the bell rung at funerals, but here the implication is that love has died.

4 The quotation 'With silence and tears' (32) at the end of the poem highlights the poem's circular structure by taking us back to a similar line (2) at the poem's beginning. Its effect suggests the speaker is not free of the feelings expressed and in future may still feel the intense sorrow of the parting.

5 The intensity of the feelings expressed tells us the poem comes from the Romantic period. For example, the imagery of touch in the quotation 'A shudder comes o'er me' (19) suggests a physical sensation, emphasising deep emotion.

6

Quotation	Technique	Effect
They know not I knew thee,/Who knew thee too well –' (21, 22)	Irony	Those who discuss the lover in the speaker's presence are unaware of the relationship between the two. In addition, not only does the speaker know the lover far better than they do, but in knowing the lover too well (or being too close) the speaker allowed himself to be betrayed – which implies, ironically, that he didn't truly know the lover at all.

7 The theme of illicit love is suggested because the relationship was carried out in 'secret' (25). It is closely connected to the theme of grief, since the speaker also grieves in 'silence' (26) or secret.

8 **Paragraph 1**: In both poems the speakers deal with a sense of disappointment and loss at the breakdown of their relationships. In 'When We Two Parted', the speaker's hurt is so acute it is linked to physical pain. The words 'Pale', 'cold' (5) 'chill' (10) and 'shudder' (19) suggest sickness, lovesickness and the death of love. Separation is also conveyed through the compound word 'broken-hearted' (3). Its meaning is heightened by the use of a hyphen, denoting separation. By contrast the speaker in 'The Farmer's Bride' expresses less emotion, but he reveals his disappointment in his choice of a wife who is young and fearful of physical closeness. He also expresses his sorrow at the prospect of no 'other in the house' (41) – a childless marriage.

Paragraph 2: Neither speaker is hopeful about their future relationship with their loved one. In 'When We Two Parted' the suggestion is that loss and separation will persist across time. If 'After long years' (30) the two should meet again, the speaker's response will one of extreme grief. In 'The Farmer's Bride' the movement of the poem slows between lines 34 and 39, and

combined with the brown oaks (34) and other autumnal imagery creates a sense of depression, implying loss of hope. However, at the end of the poem this sounds a more sinister note with the suggestion that the farmer's desire for his wife might lead to violence and abuse.

Love's Philosophy [pp. 10–11]

1 Water, as fountains, rivers and ocean 'mingle' (1) with or flow into each other. The effect is to create a feeling of intimacy and communion.

2 The repeated sibilant, particularly in stanza two, with 'kiss' and 'sea' (14), creates a soft, sensual sound associated with tenderness.

3 The natural world is used as an extended metaphor in the poem to represent unity and harmony.

4 Technique: Pathetic fallacy (or personification).

   Effect: Creates the image of human lovers kissing, increasing the level of intimacy at the end of the poem, to persuade the lover to unite with the speaker.

5 'sister-flower' (11) is a compound word and image that brings the female and nature together. Emphasising how the lover should be like nature, and unite with the speaker 'brother' (12).

6

Quotation	Technique	Effect
'high Heaven' (9)	Metonym	Represents the 'sky' as heaven, a perfect place.

7 **Paragraph 1**: The poem is written in two octaves. In the first, the speaker addresses a potential lover in order to secure a kiss. He argues that in nature nothing is 'single' (5) and pairing is natural, and ends with a question inviting the woman to join with him. In the second octave the argument is pressed home when he suggests that to reject this natural pairing is inexcusable. Finally, he asks a rhetorical question: if he is to be rejected, what then are these pairings in nature 'worth' (15)? (Implying they are worthless.) By using two octaves that repeat each other in structure and form, duality is emphasised.

Paragraph 2: The rhythm is light, and being repetitive it suits the structure and form. Enjambment (3, 4) is used to create flow, reinforcing the optimism of romantic love and nature's harmony. The rhythm's consistent beat also emphasises the logical argument, while caesura (7, 14) accentuates passionate feelings to persuade the lover. The rhyme is full ('single'/'mingle'), regular (ababcdcd) and again through repetition suits the rhythm, structure and argument.

Porphyria's Lover [pp. 12–13]

1 The poem is a dramatic monologue.

2 'did its worst to vex the lake' (4) describes the fierce and destructive wind, suggesting it is malevolent as though it were human. It also foreshadows Porphyria's murder.

3 It implies that if she has a cloak as well as a shawl and hat and gloves she is not poor, and probably comes from a wealthy background

4 Porphyria enters the cottage smoothly 'glid[ing]' (6), creating the impression of elegance. However her presence also implies a ghostly figure, foreshadowing her death. She shuts out the cold and stokes the fire, making 'the cottage warm' (9), conveying her warmth and caring personality.

ANSWERS

5

Quotation	Technique	Effect
'The rain set early in to-night' (1)	Colloquialism	*Implies the story will be told in ordinary, everyday speech.*
'vainer ties' (24)	Metaphor	*The word 'ties' suggests that Porphyria has another life or commitments, while 'vainer' suggests the speaker thinks these are frivolous, and possibly a sign of weakness*

6 It is ambiguous because the reader cannot be sure of the meaning. It could mean that the speaker is waiting for God's approval, he is waiting to be punished, he is questioning God's existence, or that he sees himself as God – all powerful.

7 Paragraph 1: In the first half of the poem the speaker is passive. Although he relates the story he describes himself as 'one so pale/ For love of' (28, 29) Porphyria, as though his love has brought a physical sickness out of a troubled longing for her. He is seated and silent (14), apparently unable to build a fire to keep warm, nor to reply to her. Porphyria, by contrast, is active. It is she who travels through the storm to visit her lover and busily tends to his needs. She is always depicted in movement, whether removing her 'dripping cloak' (11) or laying the speaker's cheek on her 'white shoulder bare' (17). Towards the end of the first half we catch a glimpse of the motive that propels him to carry out his plan in the second half of the poem. In line 25 the speaker imagines her giving herself to him eternally.

Paragraph 2: In the second half of the poem, the speaker strangles Porphyria using her long 'yellow' (39) hair, a metaphor for her beauty, his desire – and, disturbingly, the hangman's noose. His unemotional recounting of the murder conveys his belief that Porphyria will become all his, 'mine, mine' (36) permanently. It emphasises the meaning of line 25 and implies his mental instability. Now the roles are reversed. Porphyria is passive and the speaker is active, and more importantly, powerful. In his eyes she belongs to him and will remain unchanged, 'Perfectly pure and good' (37). In his delusion he has convinced himself that this was Porphyria's great desire. Although highly unlikely, it allows the speaker to believe she adored him – and now that she is dead, that can never change.

Sonnet 29 – "I think of thee!" [pp. 14–15]

1 a) Quotation: 'thee' (1)

Explanation: This is an archaic word for 'you', suggesting the poem was written in the past.

b) Quotation: 'nought' (3)

Explanation: This archaic word has been replaced by 'nothing' in contemporary English, suggesting the poem was written in the past.

2 Quotation: 'O my palm-tree' (5)

Explanation: Trees are strong and sturdy, so the palm tree stands for masculine strength.

3 Quotation: 'Drop heavily down' (11), alliteration of 'd'

The 'd' has a downward sound that emphasises the fall of the leaves.

4 The voice is passionate and focused on someone in particular, a lover. The exclamation mark emphasises longing.

5 Technique: Simile

Effect: Nature imagery shows how the speaker's thoughts about the lover cling and grow.

6 Evidence: The speaker calls the lover to 'Renew' his 'presence' (8) and come to her so that their separation can cease.

7 Nature imagery is used throughout. For example, in line 9 it creates a sensual image, in which the tree-trunk is imagined as 'bare', a metaphor for the speaker's picture of the lover.

8 Paragraph 1: 'Sonnet 29 – "I think of thee!"' is a Petrarchan sonnet, so it follows a particular form that consists of fourteen lines divided into two quatrains (or an octave) and a sestet. The quatrains have a repeating rhyme pattern: *abba*, and the sestet in this particular sonnet is *cbcbcb*. The form is a traditional one, and it focuses on a single idea or thought (rather than several kinds of ideas) that develops throughout the poem. The sonnet is frequently a love poem. Perhaps this is because the single idea suits the intense focus on the lover that is often the mark of a love poem. The traditional sonnet form has also merged with the structure of the poem.

Paragraph 2: The underlying pattern or structure of 'Sonnet 29 – "I think of thee!"' begins in the first quatrain, where the verb 'think' (1) is given emphasis because the speaker is overwhelmed by thoughts of the absent lover. In the second quatrain, her dissatisfaction increases, leading to the volta or turning point. It begins with the impatient command 'instantly' (7) and moves through line 8 coming at the end of the octave, as she calls on the lover to appear. The volta occurs just before the rhyme scheme changes with the sestet, where there is a shift in mood. The shift suggests an answer to the problem of the lover's absence: his imagined presence. This thought brings delight, culminating in the final line, where the ending contradicts the beginning, 'I think of thee' (1)/'I do not think of thee' (14) – an antithesis. The speaker no longer needs to 'think' of her lover because she is 'too near' him (14), united in spirit.

Neutral Tones [pp. 16–17]

1 The speaker recalls a memory of standing with another person by a pond in winter near a leafless tree. The sun is bleak and colourless.

2 Simile: 'grin of bitterness …/Like an ominous bird a-wing' (11, 12)

Effect: in comparing the grin to a sinister bird, it emphasises the hostility the speaker feels towards the other person, while also assuming the hostility is returned.

3 The main theme is the death of love or the breakdown of a relationship. It is supported by the speaker's comment that 'love deceives' (13), suggesting that hope has gone.

4 The regular rhythm is lost at 'between us to and fro' (7), making the line jar. This reflects the jarring relationship.

5

Quotation	Technique	Effect
'And some words played between us to and fro/On which lost the more by our love' (7, 8)	Ambiguity	It could mean: - which of us lost more from the relationship - the trivial conversation undermined the relationship further - irony; that silence would have been better, rather than trying to connect in a loveless relationship.
'eyes that rove/ Over tedious riddles …' (5, 6)	Enjambment	The run-on line emphasises 'tedious riddles' in particular, reflecting the weary mood felt by the speaker about unsolved problems in the relationship.

6 Paragraph 1: 'Love's Philosophy' is full of joy. The speaker's viewpoint is in the present tense and looks to the near future with hope, when he invites the potential lover to 'mingle' (7) or unite with him, arguing that it is only natural to do so. The viewpoint is consistent throughout the poem. By contrast in the first three stanzas of 'Neutral Tones' the speaker is looking back at an unhappy memory in which he and the other person (we can assume a lover) 'stood by a pond' (1) on a bleak day. The memory seems to sum up the relationship as it is in the present – the viewpoint the speaker shifts to in the final stanza – and in which a bitter image of the wintry scene is repeated.

Paragraph 2: In 'Love's Philosophy' nature is used to create a sense of harmony and sensuality. The 'winds of Heaven' (3) is a lofty metonym for the sky, which is joined with the quality of feeling and sensation. Nothing in nature is alone, the speaker argues. Everything is paired. The idea is used in an attempt to seduce the lover into accepting that their coming together is what the philosophy of love means, and is the most natural thing in the world. Nature in 'Neutral Tones' is grim and wintry. In the first three stanzas of the poem it is used to depict a dead world. An 'ash' (4) tree, with its double meaning and connotations of death, mirrors the dead relationship. The 'white' sun is 'chidden' (2) (scorned) by God as though the relationship was despised, suggesting the speaker is without hope.

Letters from Yorkshire [pp. 18–19]

1 The title tells us the speaker is receiving letters from Yorkshire.

2 Example: Alliteration of 'p' in '**p**lanting **p**otatoes' (1)

Effect: The 'p' makes the words sound heavy, reinforcing the idea of the heavy physical work involved in gardening.

3 Example: 'Still, it's you' (11)

Impression: Creates a conversational tone, as though the speaker is chatting to us and her friend.

4 Quotation: 'seeing the seasons' (6)

Technique 1: Sibilant 's'

Technique 2: Assonance 'ee'

Combined effect: The soft 's' sound combines with 'ee' to create a long slow, sound, suggesting a desire or longing for the natural world. The repetition of the two techniques together reinforces the effect.

5 In stanza one and lines 4 and 5, the speaker addresses the reader about her friend using the third person 'he'. In line 6 she addresses the friend in the second person: 'You out there' as though calling to or thinking of him in her mind. Either way it creates a sense of intimacy.

6 As a constructed word it could mean either that the news headlines are heart-wrenching/troubling, or that the speaker is weary of writing about news, which in turn may suggest her emotions are elsewhere, perhaps with the speaker.

7 Rhyme: 'so' (10), 'snow' (11)

Type: One end rhyme (9) that rhymes with internal rhymes (10, 11).

Effect: Helps to imitate the rise and fall (cadence) of the human voice, making the speaker's voice sound like natural speech.

8 Paragraph 1: The speaker imagines herself and her friend in contrasting situations. The friend, depicted in rural Yorkshire 'In February' (1), is taking care of his garden in winter. His 'knuckles' (3) sing and redden in the warmth as he returns indoors to write to her. The image of 'singing' (3) conveys the pleasure in the relationship, the warm knuckles, the warmth between the two. The speaker's situation is in direct contrast to her friend's. Hers is a life attached to a computer in which she feeds 'words onto a blank screen' (8), suggesting an experience she imagines being free of. When she asks 'Is [his] life more real?' (9) the implication is she feels it is (even if he does not).

Paragraph 2: Communication is one of the main themes in the poem, and it takes several forms. The speaker receives news of her friend by letter, reads the headlines and uses a computer. However, communication also has a deeper meaning. The friend in his rural world seems to be communing with nature and the soil, as he digs his garden (1), but he is also communicating with the speaker in his need to write to her about the migratory birds' return (2). The emotional connection is deep. It is especially emphasised in the final image: Their 'souls tap out messages across the icy miles' (15), reminding us of Morse code or semaphore, and the expression 'soulmate'.

The Farmer's Bride [pp. 20–21]

1 Viewpoint: It is told in the first person from the farmers' viewpoint.

Example: 'since I chose a maid' (1)

2 Tense: Present

Effect: The narrative becomes more immediate.

3 The 'berries redden' (39), suggesting blood, while 'Christmas-time' (39) refers to the birth of Christ. Blood and birth emphasise the absence of children in the marriage.

4 a) It is a narrative poem because it tells a story. 'Three Summers since' (1) suggests the opening of a story.

b) It is also a lament expressing the farmer's grief, at his marriage and the absence of children, felt particularly at 'Christmas-time' (40) when there are no 'other[s] in the house' (41).

5

Quotation	Technique	Effect
'Too young maybe –' (2)	Foreshadowing	Hints that there may be marriage problems and disappointment.
'Sweet as the first wild violets, she' (32)	Simile	Conveys the youthful age of the bride, her affinity with nature and her untamed quality.

ANSWERS

6 The image is a black and white one depicted by the magpie's feather; the earth and the 'white … rime' (38) similar to ice. There is no colour. It presents the cold, colourless farmer's life.

7 **Paragraph 1**: There is no intimacy between the farmer and his wife, and the farmer grieves for its absence. From his account, as the speaker, we are told that his bride rejected him after the wedding when 'she turned afraid' (4) not only 'Of love' but of 'all things human' (5). The last quotation implies that he sees her as an oddity, reinforced by his comment that she ''twasn't a woman' (7), meaning she does not adopt the usual intimate role of a wife. Though he admits that she may have been too young for marriage, he does not question this further. Rather he sees it as his right to lock her up when she tries to escape, which at the time the poem is set he could legally do. The wife sleeps separately from the farmer, and, with only 'a stair' (43) between them, there is the fear at the end of the poem that his desire will lead him to force himself on her.

Paragraph 2: The young wife has no voice in the poem, which not only tells us she is powerless, but also means that our view of her is depicted through the farmer's eyes. Her profound fear of him and men in particular (24), and human intimacy in general, hints at possible earlier mistreatment or abuse. Using nature imagery, the farmer compares her to a wild creature, 'a leveret' (young hare) (30), and as someone who is only happy 'to chat and play' (22) with animals. Her identification with animals further accentuates her rejection of the farmer.

Walking Away [pp. 22–23]

1 It is a thoughtful, deep mood – the speaker is recalling a memory that we know is important because he remembers the date from eighteen years ago.

2 Examples: 'walking away' (title, 7, 19), 'drifting away' (5), 'eddying away' (11)

Theme: Separation

3 'Ordeals' (15) are the difficulties we face in life. Here they are not major ones, but nevertheless they cause pain, such as the speaker's parting from his son.

4

Quotation	Technique	Effect
'like a satellite/ Wrenched from its orbit' (4, 5)	Simile	Depicts the shock of separation. The satellite is the child and the orbit is the father or family.
'irresolute clay' (15)	Metaphor	Represents human weakness – 'clay' refers to the person/body, 'irresolute' means indecision.

5 By using the enjambment 'so/Gnaws' (16, 17) the poet runs the idea quickly from one line to another to emphasise how much distress this particular parting caused the speaker, with the powerful verb 'Gnaws' starting the new line.

6 He has difficulty conveying his feelings about family ties and the pain of this particular parting from his son. However, in the last two lines he arrives at a way of conveying it: how a parent's love is shown through allowing his child to become an independent person.

7 **Paragraph 1**: The child is depicted through his father's eyes, the speaker of the poem, who is recalling a memory from eighteen years ago. We do not know the child's age at the time, but he must be young, since he has just played his 'first game of football' (4) in what we assume is his new school, a boarding school. All the images associated with the child are those that convey

vulnerability, as though he were too young to be separated from his parents. For example, he is described as a 'half-fledged thing' (8), suggesting the image of a nestling only 'half' ready to leave home. The 'f' sound may have connotations of feathers and down, adding to the sense of vulnerability. The use of 'thing' reinforces the picture a child not yet fully developed or independent.

Paragraph 2: The time of year is the end of summer, before it slips into autumn, when the leaves are beginning to turn brown, indicating change for both the child and the father. The 'touch-lines' of the school football pitch are 'new-ruled' (3) implying a new situation. They also depict a boundary, suggesting that the father is outside the new world the child will inhabit (as well as the boundary of the football pitch). The word 'touch', while conveying the love the parent feels for the child, also has other connotations, reminding us of the expression 'out of touch'. In the expression's literal sense the child will no longer be under the father's protection and must fend for himself.

Eden Rock [pp. 24–25]

1 The speaker is describing a childhood memory of his father as a young man with his dog, and his mother as a young woman waiting for him to join them by Eden Rock.

2 Tea drunk from 'tin cups' (12) and 'a screw/Of paper for a cork' (10, 11) implies that the memory comes from a much earlier period, probably between the 1920s and 1940s.

3 The final line is set apart and addresses the reader directly, creating immediacy. It highlights the surprise that the speaker feels at the way he passes from life to death.

4 Example of present continuous tense: 'are waiting' (1) suggests that the parents are continually waiting for their son to arrive.

Impact: This make us feel their presence, as if they are just out of reach, rather like spirits.

5

Quotation	Technique	Effect
' … slowly sets out/The same' (11, 12)	Sibilant	The repeated 's' in 'slowly, sets' and 'same' helps to create a soft, leisurely mood that reflects the heat of the day and the pleasure of the memory.

6 'Tweed' (3) and 'feet' (4) give a subtle emphasis to the image of the father, connecting it with the image of the mother through 'three' (5) and 'wheat' (8).

Further effect: Both are connected to 'Eden' (Paradise) in line 1.

7 It could represent the Christian holy trinity: God, Christ and the Holy Ghost, as well as the Virgin Mary, Joseph and Jesus. It could also be the human family – the speaker, mother and father. However, the metaphor reinforces the idea of an otherworldly scene.

8 **Paragraph 1**: The speaker is imaging himself crossing the border or 'the drifted stream' (15) between life and death. He imagines his parents on the other side 'waiting for' (1) him, an expression of their love. Therefore, the two main themes are death and love. The imagery is often religious. The title and reference in the first line conjures up a picture of the Garden of Eden, a symbol of Paradise, a place of perfection and contentment. The mother's 'hair, the colour of wheat' (8) shines, suggesting a halo and an angelic vision, and the sky is a brilliant white (13). Both these images reinforce the theme of love in the parental and religious sense.

Paragraph 2: 'Eden Rock' (1), where the parents are waiting, is also part of a childhood memory. The speaker recalls a picnic in which his father as a young man wears his 'Irish Tweed' (3) suit, suggesting a special family occasion. His mother wears 'a sprigged dress' (5), evoking a rural or garden setting, reinforcing the early image of the Garden of Eden. A further religious image is 'the stiff white cloth' (7), on which the picnic is set, conjuring up not only purity, but also the cloth of Holy Communion in the Christian religion. This in turn reinforces the idea of communion or a coming together with the parents. The speaker's memory of himself as a child is that he must cross the stream to where his parents are, and at the end of the poem the adult speaker and the child merge as he prepares to cross over to 'the other bank' (17), or from life to death.

Follower [pp. 26–27]

1 'Follower' (title) describes both the son and the father at different times of their lives. The son as a child followed his father around, and the father as an old man follows his son.

2 The speaker describes his father working on the land with a horse and plough.

3 Quotation: 'I wanted to grow up and plough/To close one eye, stiffen my arm' (17, 18)

   Explanation: In his child-like way, the child is mimicking the father, believing this was how he ploughed a field, not understanding the skill involved.

4 The quatrains seem to follow the repetitive movement of the plough in its 'Dipping and rising' (16). The effect is emphasised by frequent enjambment. In one case the line runs on into the next stanza, so that 'with a single pluck/Of reins' (8, 9) the reader feels the plough's turn as it comes back down the field.

5 Type of metre: Iambic tetrameter (i.e. four feet, each consisting of a weak syllable followed by a strong one).

   Effect: This makes a steady, regular rhythm that suits the steady, repetitive movement of the plough.

6 Full rhyme: 'arm'/'farm' (18, 20)

   Half rhyme: 'plough'/'follow' (17, 19)

   Effect: The full and half rhyme help to work with the metre to reinforce the regular beat. If there had been only full rhyme, this might have produced too bouncy a rhythm, which would not have suited the thoughtful nature of the poem.

7 Meaning 1 and effect: 'the trail of waves left by a ship' (which refers back to the nautical image in line 7). It reveals the way in which the child is left behind by the father's energetic ploughing.

   Meaning 2 and effect: A vigil for the dead. Foreshadows the father's decline.

8 **Paragraph 1**: As a child, the speaker adored his father. 'An expert' (5) ploughman, the images of him present a man at one with the land. In a nautical image, the speaker remembers how his father's 'shoulders globed like a full sail strung/Between the shafts and the furrow' (2, 3). The first image, a simile, conveys the father's powerful muscles as well as the billowing of his shirt in the wind like a sail. The second image presents the 'shafts' of the plough cutting the earth like a ship ploughing through the waves, while the furrow is like the trail of water left behind. This complex image portrays both the father's strength and skill, and in a plain, explicit line, the speaker recalls how he 'wanted to grow up and plough' (17); to be like his hero.

   Paragraph 2: The final lines of the poem (23, 24) are the key to an understanding of the son as an adult and his relationship with his father. The mood has changed. The positions seem to have reversed. Where the child was in the father's way,

'tripping, falling' and being 'a nuisance' (21), it is now the father, a 'stumbling' (23) old man who pesters the son, 'and will not go away' (24); will not leave the son alone. However, it can be argued that the relationship is more complex. The powerful impression the father left on the child may still be at work in the adult mind. The speaker's overwhelming desire to be like his father, and his acceptance that he lacks his physical talent may still gnaw at the son. The words 'will not go away' might therefore mean the speaker is haunted by his sense of failure. Since it will not leave him, he remains in his father's 'broad shadow' (20).

Mother, any distance [pp. 28–29]

1 The setting is the son's new home, into which he hasn't yet moved. His mother has come to help him take measurements around the house.

2 Meaning 1: The generation gap.

   Meaning 2: The shared history between the mother and son, and linked to this the increased emotional distance between mother and son in the future.

3 Example: 'space-walk' (9)

   Impact: Suggests an astronaut tethered to the 'mother' craft, as the son is tethered to the mother by the tape measure.

4 Meaning: The speaker is addressing his mother, saying that help is needed for a task that is anything more than a span (the gap between the little finger and the thumb, when the hand is fully extended).

   Effect: Because a span is only short, it suggests the mother's need to help her son with anything more than the smallest of tasks. The comment could be read as sardonic, as if the son is well aware of and irritated by his mother's need to help.

5

Quotation	Technique	Effect
'something/has to give' (10, 11)	Colloquialism	Meaning something will break under the build-up of pressure, suggesting that something will break in the relationship between mother and son (as well as the tape measure breaking).
'fingertips still pinch' (12)	Assonance	The short 'i' sound emphasises the mother's attempt to cling onto her son.

6 The irregular lines, particularly lines 7 to 11, reflect the irregular unreeling of the tape measure as the speaker climbs to the attic.

7 **Paragraph 1**: In 'Follower' the speaker as a child hero-worshipped his father. He wanted, like him, to develop his own skill working on the land with the horse plough. His father could map 'the furrow exactly' (12), meaning he could keep a straight furrow while keeping the depth and turning of the soil consistent. This reveals his expertise, to the admiration of his small son. In 'Mother, any distance' the speaker's attitude to his mother is one of irritation when she helps him take measurements in his new home. She holds one end of the measuring tape and he holds the other, 'recording length,/reporting metres … back to base' (5, 6), implying that she is in control. As the son moves upstairs away from his mother, the tape becomes stretched 'to breaking point' (10), emphasising not only the tension between them, but also his need for separation. The tape measure is an extended metaphor for connection, and can, for example, be seen as the umbilical cord that holds a mother to her baby, the implication being that the mother cannot let go of her son and encourage him to lead his own life.

ANSWERS

Paragraph 2: The relationship between son and father changes in 'Follower'. As an adult the speaker's attitude, like the son in 'Mother, any distance', is one of irritation with his elderly father. It is he who keeps following now 'and will not go away' (24), showing a reversal of roles. But it may also be an admission that the speaker cannot come to terms with his own lack of physical skill; that his father's expertise haunts him, as well as his sorrow at the differences between them. We sense that the father is a man of few words (none of his speech is reported) who is focused on his physical work. The son, by contrast, recalls his own talkative nature. They seem to be opposites. At the end of 'Mother, any distance', the speaker is faced with a dilemma. He feels the need to break free of his mother's dominance, but we are not sure he can. From the confines of the attic he reaches towards a hatch that opens onto a panoramic view of 'an endless sky' (14), a powerful metaphor signifying independence and life beyond his mother's constraints. Whether or not he can snatch his freedom, we do not know.

Before You Were Mine [pp. 30–31]

1 Quotation: 'in the ballroom with the thousand eyes' (7)

2 Example: 'I knew you would dance/like that' (8, 9)

Technique 1: the enjambment (8) that stops abruptly in line 9

Technique 2: (caesura) emphasises the mother's carefree attitude to life and the speaker's awareness of this.

3 The colloquial expression 'a hiding for the late one' (10). This suggests the language of a Scottish community, which is probably working class. The word 'hiding' is Scottish dialect for physical punishment, so the mother as a young woman is being punished by her mother for being late home.

4 Quotation: 'Your polka-dot dress blows round your legs. Marilyn' (5)

Historical period: The context is the 1950s and the famous pose is of the film star Marilyn Monroe.

Explanation: It implies the mother was young in the 1950s and also reinforces a mood of glamour, which the daughter associates with her mother's youth.

5

Quotation	Technique	Effect
'the fizzy, movie tomorrows' (7)	Metaphor	*Suggesting romantic possibilities of being taking to the cinema – 'fizzy' suggests sparkling wine.*
'stamping stars' (17)	Connotation	*The image has associations with the Hollywood Walk of Fame, where famous celebrities have their names stamped on stars. The effect is to reinforce the idea of glamour through the senses of sound and touch as well as sight, as the feet hit the pavement.*

6 Image: 'clear as scent' (14)

Effect 1: 'scent' appeals to the sense of smell, the most potent of the senses related to memory, so the sight–sense relationship makes the image particularly potent.

Effect 2: The intense image suggests the speaker's love for her mother.

7 **Paragraph 1:** The poem opens with the speaker addressing her mother, but it is from a state 'ten years' (1) before birth, and she is imagining her mother's life before the speaker was born and is probably looking at a photograph. He mother is depicted as a light-hearted, playful teenager or young woman laughing at the corner of a street with her 'pals' 'Maggie McGeeney and Jean Duff' (2). The voice is not a child's. It is an adult voice – affectionate but possessive. The title 'Before You Were Mine' reverses the normal mother–child relationship. We might expect the mother to use these words about her child, and a child to say 'Before I was yours'. However the voice's possessive quality suits its commanding, all-seeing (omniscient) nature.

Paragraph 2: This omniscient nature governs the structure of the poem. In line 12 for example, the voice shifts to the speaker's childhood years when she is playing with her mother's 'high-heeled red shoes'. Then in line 13 the reader is brought into the present when the speaker imagines how her mother's 'ghost clatters toward' her, in what we can assume are the red shoes. The speaker's mood shifts very slightly. The image is vivid and moving; vivid because the speaker can see her mother clearly in her mind's eye, and yet, since the mother is a ghost, the speaker cannot touch her. In stanza four the voice shifts back to childhood memories, but maintains a sense of longing: 'Even then/I wanted the bold girl' (17, 18). The last line takes us back to the title, creating a circular effect, as though the special memory of the mother will never leave the speaker.

Winter Swans [pp. 32–33]

1 The speaker addresses his lover, and the reader feels as if they are listening.

2 Quotation: 'with a show of tipping in unison' (8)

Feeling/emotion: The reader feels that the swans' pairing is harmonious and a reminder to the couple of commitment in a relationship.

3 Example: 'slow-stepping in the lake's shingle and sand' (16)

Effect: Creates a softer, gentler sound and mood, as the couple move towards reconciliation.

4 The poem is written in tercets in stanzas one to six, and moves easily from stanza to stanza through skilful use of enjambment. The effect suggests the walk around the lake.

5 'gulping' (5) suggests struggling for breath, and this in turn implies that the relationship between the speaker and his partner is struggling to survive.

6

Quotation	Technique	Effect
'The clouds had given their all' (1)	Pathetic fallacy	*The clouds are given a human trait, suggesting that they were determined to rain as though they had a conscious purpose.*
The swans like 'porcelain' (14)	Metaphor	*Porcelain is white and represents the swans, but also the idea of marriage. Porcelain breaks easily, suggesting that care must be taken in relationships.*

7 **Paragraph 1:** The poem opens as the speaker recalls a walk with his partner around a lake after it has been raining heavily for two days. The track is saturated, 'waterlogged' (4), implying that the relationship between the speaker and his partner is bogged down and threatened by disagreement. As the two walk along the track silent and apart (reinforcing the idea of separation) a pair of swans arrive on the lake. Together the swans tip their heads in the water and then bob up again together, 'like boats righting in rough weather' (12). The simile illustrates that the trouble or 'rough weather' in the relationship between the couple can be overcome.

Paragraph 2: The swans suggest the perspective the couple need to remind themselves of their commitment to each other. '"They mate for life"' (13), the speaker's partner says as the swans leave, breaking the silence between the couple. In a second simile, the gesture of holding hands is compared to 'a pair of wings settling after flight' (20). This simile, particularly through the noun 'flight', also suggests that the relationship, which was slipping away from the couple, is now rescued. The image of the swans therefore becomes a motif for commitment that runs from stanza three, when the swans first appear, to the end of the poem.

Singh Song! [pp. 34–35]

1 The speaker, a young man, runs one of his father's grocery shops and is expected to work through the day without a break, but when there are no customers he locks the shop door.

2 Internal rhyme: There is an internal rhyme, 'Singh' and 'bin' (12), which is repeated and is part of the chorus.

Mood: It helps to create the rise and fall of the voice (cadence), making the chorus sound musical.

3 The caesura seems to be used to create a pause as a signal to the reader that there is a shift of focus, for example to a new event or depiction.

Thinking more deeply

4 It is a way of showing us that the speaker is uninterested in his business and not keen to make money, challenging the stereotype of the Asian shopkeeper. The chorus has a bouncy rhythm and helps create a comic mood.

5

Quotation	Technique	Effect
'Singh' (title)	Pun	Singh is the surname of all Sikh men; 'sing-song' is slang for a voice that has a marked rise and fall. It is a negative stereotype.
'pinnie' (10)	Idiom, saying or expression	Uses a common expression, making the speaker believable; 'pinnie' is short for 'pinafore', an apron.

6 'vee' (6, 7, 8, 9) is a dialect word for 'we' and is repeated to emphasise how close the speaker feels to his new bride as they share their new life together.

7 **Paragraph 1:** The speaker's description of his bride is full and varied. He depicts her as sexually confident in stanza five, when they share Asian food after making love. A midnight exchange, while revealing her playful, romantic side, also revolves around money and the cost of the 'moon', (52) suggesting a mercenary aspect to her nature. She is independent-minded, preferring multicultural fashion – with, for example, a red punk haircut, a Scottish tartan for her sari and a building worker's jacket. In stanza five, she has no qualms about swearing at or making fun of her in-laws. Her disregard for them suggests a rebellious nature, though not one her husband objects to. He describes her affectionately throughout. She has 'di tummy ov a teddy' (29), an image that implies a softness to her character. However, she also has the eyes 'ov a gun' (28): direct, exact and lethal.

Paragraph 2: The relationship between the two suggests that the marriage is an open one. The bride visits her 'Sikh lover' (20) website in stanza four. Here, the use of 'mouse' (19) and 'cat' (20) is ambiguous – 'playing wid di mouse' (19) can have a double meaning, referring to both the computer device and the idiom 'playing cat or mouse', or teasing. 'cat' implies the men she is 'netting' (20) or catching on the site. But is she also a 'cat' playing

with the men, the 'mice'? Whether or not the contact goes beyond the website is unclear, but booking the men for 'di meat at di cheese ov her price' (21) implies payment for extramarital relations, to which the speaker expresses no objections. Whatever the interpretation, it challenges the stereotypical version of the submissive Asian wife.

Climbing My Grandfather [pp. 36–37]

1 It suggests a child climbing up onto his grandfather's lap, or perhaps climbing up him as small children do, especially when a relation is seated.

2 He has hands dirty from the soil and his nails are splintered, giving the impression of a man who worked on the land and did manual work, perhaps as a gardener or farmer.

3 There is only one stanza of twenty-seven lines, creating a continuous poem that helps reinforce the idea of a mountain.

4 The speaker begins the journey by stepping onto his grandfather's shoes ('old brogues', line 2), which suggests 'feet' and also the journey beginning at the foot of the mountain. The shoes are 'dusty and cracked' (2), implying that the grandfather cared little for his appearance. However, it can also suggest the beginning of a dry mountain track.

5 The geographical terms show the poet had a good knowledge of landscape, reflected for example in the landform 'scar' (11), meaning a protruding rocky place. It helps to contribute to the sense of climbing a mountain, but also helps to build a picture of the grandfather, since 'scar' also means the site of an old wound, which emphasises his age and experience. The geographical features in the poem are part of the extended metaphor of the mountain representing the grandfather.

6

Quotation	Technique	Effect
'belt' (6)	Double meaning	Refers to a group of mountain ranges and also to the belt around the grandfather's waist. The double meaning helps to reinforce the idea of the mountain representing the grandfather (an extended metaphor).
'stare into his brown eyes, watch a pupil / slowly open and close' (19, 20)	Sibilant	Soft 's' emphasises the gentle exploration of the grandfather's eyes, as the speaker searches for him.

7 **Paragraph 1:** The structure of the poem is a journey that the speaker takes in order to get closer to his dead grandfather. This we can assume is a main goal. It follows the climb that a mountaineer might take from starting point to summit. There are various stages in what is a strenuous climb, 'without a rope or net' (1), implying it is a dangerous one emotionally. It begins with the grandfather's well-worn shoes, then travels up and across different examples of the grandfather's clothes and physical features. These are compared to different mountain landforms (such as the jutting rock formation 'overhanging', 5) so that the mountain becomes an extended metaphor for the grandfather. The journey ends at the summit, which brings relief, but also a sense of achievement, suggesting that the speaker has succeeded in achieving his goal.

Paragraph 2: For the speaker, the journey is a way of recovering memories of his grandfather. The metaphor 'trying to get a grip' (4) suggests the 'grip' on the mountain, but also an attempt to

ANSWERS

recover an image of his grandfather. Some memories may be painful, as implied by the reference to the perils of climbing. But there are potentially positive ones too; borne out, for example, when the speaker halts at his grandfather's 'still firm shoulder' (13). The image portrays a physically strong elderly man, and a reliable one. The memories also reflect the joy the relationship brought. At the end of the journey the speaker feels the grandfather's 'good heart' beating (27), suggesting closeness and love. Perhaps the journey is similar to the way a mountaineer experiences a dangerous climb, but also reflects on the nature of the mountain and the joy it brings.

PART THREE: THEMES AND CONTEXTS [PP. 39–51]

Themes: Breakdown and betrayal [p. 39]

1 The title suggests lack of colour and unimportance. It seems to convey the speaker's indifference to the relationship, which is completely broken.

2 We are told that 'The clouds had given their all' (1), depicting extreme weather. The image is a pathetic fallacy which implies that the couple have also 'given their all' at quarrelling, which in turn suggests a breakdown, albeit temporary, in the relationship.

3 a) Quotation from 'The Farmer's Bride': 'Like the shut of a winter's day' (6)

Link to theme: Breakdown. The simile refers to the wife's response to her husband after the marriage, suggesting the relationship is broken from the beginning.

Effect: 'shut' implies that the wife's response is clear; that there is no hope of an intimate relationship developing. 'winter' implies 'cold', reinforcing the coldness of the wife's response to her husband.

b) Quotation from 'When We Two Parted': 'That thy heart could forget,/Thy spirit deceive' (27, 28)

Link to theme: Betrayal. The speaker is distressed that the lover could forget him, and by implication easily forget him, so that he feels betrayed.

Effect: Someone's 'spirit' can be thought of as their essential core or essence. From the reader's point of view the lover's spirit seems to be dishonest, suggesting that the lover's feelings for the speaker were never deep.

Themes: Family ties [pp. 40–41]

1 'Walking Away'. The father recalls his son's first day at a new school.

2 The line evokes a domestic or family scene. The use of 'same' and the detail given of the cups, 'tin' and 'blue' (12), suggest a strong family memory.

3 a) Quotation from 'Follower': 'I stumbled in his hob-nailed wake' (13)

Link to theme: The speaker as a small unsteady child followed behind his father the ploughman, reflecting the theme of 'family ties'.

Effect: 'stumbled' suggests that the speaker as an adult lacks his father's physical skills as he follows in his trail or 'wake'.

b) Quotation from 'Before You Were Mine': 'Even then/I wanted the bold girl winking in Portobello' (17, 18)

Link to theme: The speaker describes how as a child (as well as in the present) she imagined her mother as a teenager or young woman in Portobello, Scotland.

Effect: It is an affectionate portrayal of the mother, who appeals to the child because she seems spirited, implied by 'bold', and fun-loving, implied by 'winking'.

4

Quotation	Effect
'place my feet /gently in the old stitches' (11, 12)	It depicts the speaker's love for his grandfather. The adverb 'gently' suggests care and consideration.

5

Quotation	Effect
'They are waiting for me somewhere beyond Eden Rock' (1)	The opening words suggest a connection still exists between the speaker and his parents, who are 'beyond' or in the afterlife ('Eden').

6 **Paragraph 1**: In 'Walking Away', the 'hesitant figure' (11) that describes the child as he walks towards what is apparently a boarding school could just as well describe the speaker's feelings about the parting from his son. What seems to trouble the speaker in particular is his son's age. The child is only 'half-fledged' (8), like a baby bird not fully developed. The vivid simile suggests vulnerability, a child too young to leave home. The mood is reinforced in the third stanza through another simile of the child moving haphazardly like a sycamore seed (12), as though unsure of his direction. Perhaps there is also a sense of guilt in the speaker's tone? In the final verse, the powerful verb 'Gnaws' (17), suggesting worry, describes how the memory of the parting has persisted over years.

Paragraph 2: By contrast the speaker in 'Mother, any distance' is the adult son, so the mother's behaviour is presented through his eyes, not hers. When her son plans his move to a new home she is there to help take measurements. The extended metaphor of the tape measure signifies the connection between them, which is stretched 'to breaking point' (10), suggesting the tension between them. While he proceeds upstairs, her 'fingertips still pinch' (12) the end of the tape measure. She clings onto it fiercely, which conveys a strong sense in the reader's mind of someone who cannot let go emotionally. She seems to be the kind of mother who needs to be in control, or perhaps to feel needed as her son tries to forge a life of his own.

Themes: Love and desire [pp. 42–43]

1 'When We Two Parted': The speaker's lover has betrayed him. 'The Farmer's Bride': The farmer's love for his young wife is not returned; it is unrequited.

2 The nature of the relationship between the speaker and her friend is ambiguous. On the one hand the use of the word 'souls' (15) and its association with 'soulmate' suggests a deep connection. On the other hand we are told 'It's not romance' (5), which implies there is no physical intimacy between them, so we can regard the friendship as deep affection, if not more.

3 a) Quotation from 'Love's Philosophy': 'what are all these kissings worth,/If thou kiss not me?' (15, 16)

Link to theme: The kind of love expressed is seduction. The speaker asks the potential lover to unite with him physically.

Effect: The rhetorical question presents the reader, as well as the lover, with the final point in the argument: that nature's unity is worth nothing if the speaker cannot unite with the loved one.

b) Quotation from 'Sonnet 29 – "I think of thee!"': 'I will not have my thoughts instead of thee' (6)

Link to theme: The kind of love expressed is passionate love. The speaker expresses a deep need to have her lover near, rather than merely imagining him.

Effect: The speaker is building towards the turning point of the sonnet (volta) in which she will demand that her lover come to her, so at this point the quotation is a declaration that sounds a note of urgency. Her thoughts of him, the speaker is saying, are no substitute for his presence.

4

Theme	Quotation	Effect
Love and desire – delusion	'Porphyria worshipped me' (33)	The speaker utters these words just before he murders Porphyria. It becomes clear to the reader that he is under the delusion that her love for him was like devotion to a god.

5

Theme	Quotation	Effect
Love and desire – reuniting	'I noticed our hands, that had, somehow,/swum the distance between us' (17, 18)	'swum' suggests an image of the swans. Their partnership has had a subtle influence on the couple, who are bridging the divide between them and rekindling their love for each other.

6 Paragraph 1: The speakers in the poems are both the husbands, and they express very different experiences of married life. In 'The Farmer's Bride', the young wife sleeps separately from her husband 'in the attic' (42), which reveals the lack of intimacy between them. The reader sees how the farmer's mood is one of surprise and distress, conveyed in the explicit words 'she turned afraid/Of love and me' (4, 5). His distress also focuses, in stanza five, on the lack of children in the marriage. By contrast the shopkeeper and speaker in 'Singh Song!' is happy in stanzas one and two to shut the shop during the day and visit his wife upstairs for love, romance and, importantly, sharing. The last is emphasised when they share food, in the repeated lines 'vee share' (6, 7) (dialect for 'we share'). This suggests to the reader that friendship as well as love is part of their marriage.

Paragraph 2: Throughout 'Singh Song!' the shopkeeper's description of his marriage is scattered with words of affection, such as the 'tickle' of his 'bride' (35). His marriage appears to be a happy, open relationship in which he tolerates his wife 'effing' (swearing) at his 'mum' (23) and visiting her 'Sikh lover' (20) website. On the other hand, the farmer lacks tolerance. He does not consider that the wife's fear of 'men-folk' (24) hints at earlier abuse. As a husband the reader feels that the farmer is dominant in the marriage (a common attitude in the nineteenth century, the period in which the poem is set) to the extent that he is prepared to lock her up when she tries to escape (19). The marriage is an unhappy one, and by the end of the poem we do not know whether or not the farmer will force his young wife to have intimate relations.

Themes: Separation and distance [p. 44]

1 All the poems deal with separation in some form, except 'Singh Song!', where the theme is romance and affection between a married couple. There is some parental conflict, but no suggestion that this has led to separation.

2 The final line of each quatrain is set apart from the others, making it at odds with the other lines. This in turn implies that the two people in the relationship are at odds, helping to create a mood of disconnectedness and resentment.

3 Quotation from 'Letters from Yorkshire': 'Still, it's you/who sends me word of that other world' (11, 12)

Link to theme: The friend is some distance in time and place away from the speaker. The letters bridge the gap between the speaker and her friend.

Effect: 'other world' (12) conjures up an image of distant planets, accentuating the distance in miles between the speaker and her friend. However, the friend connects with the speaker through his 'word(s)'/letters (12). The enjambment in which 'you' is given emphasis (11) also adds to the impression that the friends are close.

4 Quotation: 'They beckon to me from the other bank' (17) – links with death.

Quotation: 'I reach/towards a hatch that opens on an endless sky/to fall or fly' (13–15) – links with growing apart.

Effect for 'Eden Rock': The reader becomes aware of the symbolic nature of the stream as the river that separates life and death. This has connotations of the River Styx in Greek mythology, which separates Earth and the Underworld (Hades).

Effect for 'Mother, any distance': The speaker is struggling to separate from his mother, suggested in the image of the opening hatch, in his bid for freedom, 'the endless sky' (14). However he is uncertain of the future and does not know whether he will fail – 'fall', or succeed – 'fly' (15).

Themes: The natural world [p. 45]

1 a) 'The Farmer's Bride' has a farm setting.

b) 'Porphyria's Lover' is set near trees and a lake.

2 The last line depicts a motionless scene. There is no mention of the water moving, and the 'grey' leaves appear dead. Both these natural features reflect the deadness of the relationship.

3 a) Quotation from 'Sonnet 29 "I think of thee!"': 'the straggling green' (4)

Technique: Metaphor

Effect: The quotation is a metaphor for the vine leaves. In turn the vine leaves are a metaphor for the nature of the speaker's rambling thoughts and feelings about her lover.

b) Quotation from 'Letters from Yorkshire': 'lapwings return' (2)

Technique: Connotation

Effect: The 'lapwings' returning for the spring season connotes distances covered and boundaries crossed. They remind the reader of the friend's letters, which do the same.

Themes: Death, time and memory [pp. 46–47]

1 'Before You Were Mine', in which the speaker imagines her mother's life before she had given birth.

2 The speaker as an adult is trying to recover a memory from the past, a childhood memory of his grandfather who his now dead. By exploring the enduring memory the speaker recovers 'the slow pulse of his good heart' (27). 'pulse' suggests a 'heart' that is beating, conveying the sense that his grandfather is alive now, by being alive in the speaker's memory.

3 a) Quotation from 'Porphyria's Lover': 'And all night long we have not stirred' (59)

Link to theme of death: The speaker is sitting with Porphyria, whom he has murdered.

Effect: The words 'all night long' and 'have not stirred' reinforce the image of the dead Porphyria. However they also present us with the speaker who, immobile himself, seems to mirror her death, and so he finds some perverted kind of peace.

b) Quotation from 'The Farmer's Bride': 'On the black earth spread white with rime' (38)

Link to theme of death: The image is of winter, a time when the natural world seems dead.

Effect: The image presents a lifeless scene in which the earth is 'black', not green and fruitful, and is covered with ice, suggesting the dead relationship between the farmer and his wife.

ANSWERS

4

Quotation	Effect
'It is eighteen years ago, almost to the day –' (1)	The memory was from a time many years ago, and the accuracy of the timing since it was 'almost to the day', emphasises the importance of the memory.

5

Quotation	Effect
'If I should meet thee/ After long years' (29, 30)	The emphasis on 'long' tells us that there will be many years before the speaker is likely to meet the ex-lover again. However, it also implies that those years will seem especially 'long' because he will still be grieving for the lost relationship.

6 Paragraph 1: Memory is a strong theme throughout 'Neutral Tones'. In the first stanza details of a potent memory are given: the pond, the sun and the tree all portray an unsatisfactory relationship. The image of the 'starving' (3) earth, for example, suggests to the reader that the relationship was already dying at the time. This is confirmed in the second and third stanzas, where the speaker recollects with bitterness the other person's features. The memory seems to have been long-standing. 'Since then' (13) brings us into the present in the final stanza. Nothing has improved. There is no resolution to the difficulties, and the memory endures.

Paragraph 2: In 'Eden Rock' a potent memory is also evoked and, as in 'Neutral Tones', it persists throughout the poem. However it is a childhood memory, and a joyful one, of a picnic on a sunny day. The speaker's father twirls a stone across the stream 'Leisurely' (16), suggesting not only 'unhurried' but the contentment and peace the memory brings. The memory serves as a connection from the past through to the present and beyond into the hereafter and Eden (1), a symbol of Paradise. The speaker is thinking about his own death and how he will be united with his parents as though he were as innocent as a child, which has connotations of the Christian belief of how one must be to enter Heaven.

Contexts: The Romantics and Victorians [p. 48]

1 Romantic poem: 'When We Two Parted' or 'Love's Philosophy'

Victorian poem: 'Sonnet 29 – "I think of thee!"', 'Porphyria's Lover', 'Neutral Tones' or 'The Farmer's Bride'

2 For the Romantic poets, like Shelley, nature was pure and honest and a way of expressing strong feelings. Choosing nature imagery was a way of reacting against the Industrial Revolution and mass production of the eighteenth and nineteenth centuries, which the Romantics felt abused nature (what we today would call the environment).

3 Quotation from 'When We Two Parted': 'Long, long shall I rue thee' (23)

Explanation: The quotation expresses intense feelings, a common feature of Romanticism.

Effect: The speaker expresses his feelings directly to the lover, and the repetition of 'long' helps to drive home how strong his feelings of distress are. 'rue' has connotations with 'raw', emphasising the rawness of the hurt felt.

4 Archaic language such as 'maid' (1) for 'young woman', 'bide' (3) meaning 'sit waiting', and 'abed' (11) for 'in bed', tells us the poem is likely to be set in the Victorian period. Also such words as 'lanterns' (16) suggest a time before battery-powered torches were available.

Contexts: The Gothic [p. 49]

1 It was fashionable in the nineteenth century, and is sometimes called the Victorian Gothic.

2 The setting of 'Porphyria's Lover' is a lonely, isolated cottage in a dramatic landscape. The weather is sinister, particularly the wind, and is given human feelings (i.e. pathetic fallacy is used). Both these features are typical of the Gothic, which emphasises horror.

3 Quotation from 'Porphyria's Lover': '... her cheek once more/ Blushed bright beneath my burning kiss' (47, 48)

Explanation: The action shows how the speaker is drawn to the corpse and seems unable to understand the gravity of his crime. An unstable mind is often a feature of the Gothic.

Effect: The quotation is a gruesome image of intimacy between the speaker and his murdered victim, and is very unsettling for the reader.

4 Quotation: 'As a shut bud that holds a bee' (43) – links with crime, murder.

Technique: It is a simile that depicts Porphyria's murder.

Effect: In a literal sense the bee is imprisoned, helpless and bound to die, so it drives home to the reader the horror of Porphyria's death.

Contexts: Portrayal of women [p. 50]

1 'Singh Song!'

2 References to 'George Square' (13) in Glasgow and the 'Portobello' (18) district of Edinburgh tell us the setting is Scotland. In the speaker's mind these Scottish cities are the setting for 'the bold girl' (18), suggesting the mother's spirited youth. The mood created is one of excitement and youthful possibility.

3 a) Quotation from 'The Farmer's Bride': '... I chose a maid/Too young maybe' (1, 2)

This reveals: it is the farmer, the man, who chooses a wife of whatever age.

Context: Generally speaking, marriage was not an equal partnership in Victorian society. It was considered a woman's duty to obey her husband.

b) Quotation from 'Singh Song!': 'my bride/she hav a red crew cut' (30, 31)

This reveals: a bride who makes her own choices, regardless of what others think.

Context: The poem is a contemporary poem that presents us with an independent-minded British Asian woman. It also challenges the stereotypical view that British Asian wives are submissive.

PART FOUR: FORM, STRUCTURE AND LANGUAGE [pp. 52–63]

Form and structure [pp. 52–54]

1 'The Farmer's Bride' and 'Porphyria's Lover'

2 'When We Two Parted' and 'Love's Philosophy'

3 The stanzas in 'Letters from Yorkshire' are laid out in tercets (sets of three lines).

4 Sonnets usually have fourteen lines, and often end in a rhyming couplet. This poem starts off in sonnet form and does have the end couplet. However, 'Mother any distance' differs from this because lines 10 and 14 run on into the next lines to create fifteen lines. Lines 10 and 11 ('something/has to give') could be applied to stretching the sonnet form as well as the tension between mother and son. The poem is an ambiguous sonnet, perhaps reflecting the nature of the speaker's feelings about breaking free of his mother.

5

Poem	Form	Effect
'Climbing My Grandfather'	Free verse	The poem has no regular rhythm and is not divided into stanzas or verses. The poet has chosen to lay out his poem in a long column that suggests climbing a mountain or a steep gradient.
'Singh Song!'	Poem or song with chorus	The chorus in particular gives the poem its musicality. The repetition creates a bouncy, tuneful rhythm.

6 The speaker decides to do the climb without 'a rope or net' (1), meaning there will be no safety net if he should fall. It implies that the climb is dangerous emotionally, because he will be remembering his dead grandfather and may have to face painful memories.

7 In stanza five winter is depicted and the rhythm slows from the fast pace of stanza four and the steady pace of the previous stanzas. The mood is affected. It becomes gloomy as the farmer contemplates the lack of children in the marriage.

8 Couplets are often associated with love poems, and often help to bring the poem to a neat resolution. In 'Singh Song!' the four couplets work with the repeated rhyme 'say' and 'baby' and help to shift the busy, jolly mood of the earlier verses to a slower, more romantic mood.

9 The last stanza of 'Winter Swans' is a couplet. The poem is a love song and traditionally (as in the sonnet) love poems end with a couplet. It also suggests that the speaker and his partner are together again.

10 The last line is set apart to give emphasis, perhaps because the speaker in his imagination is about to die and meet his parents in Paradise. The space between the last line and the previous one also reinforces how the speaker is separated from his parents by the stream, until he crosses it. There is also a change in mood to one of greater immediacy as the speaker shifts from describing events to expressing his feelings more directly.

11 **Paragraph 1**: 'Porphyria's Lover' is a dramatic monologue in which a single voice tells a story, so it is also a narrative poem. The persona, a strong voice that creates a sense of character, is the murderer's voice, although we do not realise this until the murder occurs. We follow the speaker's words and actions and from the first line, 'The rain set early in to-night', we recognise the everyday language, as though the speaker was talking directly to us about the weather. The poem is presented in one long verse to create the impression of a speech being given, and is similar to a monologue spoken by an actor on stage addressing the audience. It creates a sense of intimacy, which makes the act of murder in the poem all the more shocking.

Paragraph 2: There is no other voice but the speaker's, which is typical of the dramatic monologue. Porphyria either remains silent or has been silenced, so the reader is dependent on the speaker for information. We never know how Porphyria feels, or how she views herself or her circumstances. This becomes particularly important at the turning point when the second half of the monologue begins. The speaker finds 'A thing to do' (38), which becomes an act of murder. We see how unstable he is and therefore how unreliable as a narrator. The effect is highly disturbing, particularly since the voice has been so intimate. As the monologue continues, so the drama increases until at the end we realise that the speaker is completely out of touch with reality.

Rhyme, rhythm and sound [pp. 55–56]

1 *abbacdcdd*

2 Full rhyme occurs at the end of the first, third and fifth line of each stanza.

3 The rhythm is regular, at least as far as the stressed beat occurs, which is twice in each line. It is an especially strong, heavy beat, rather like a chant or lament or a slow funeral march. The rhythm suits the mood of the poem, in which the speaker is lamenting the death of love and the grief of a failed relationship.

4 Iambic pentameter is a line of poetry that has an unstressed syllable followed by a stressed one (iambic) for five feet (pentameter). Each foot is a unit made up of one unstressed and stressed syllable. Traditional dramatic monologues are written in iambic pentameter. It is the most common metre in English because it follows the rhythms of speech and makes the voice seem natural, as suits the storytelling aspect of the poem here.

5

Technique	Example/reference	Effect
Caesura in 'The Farmer's Bride' (44)	'Betwixt us. Oh! my God!'	The heavy use of the pause in the line emphasises the wife's presence in the attic nearby ('Betwixt us') and the farmer's increasing desire for her.
Enjambment in 'Love's Philosophy' (the first octave)	It occurs in line 1, running into line 2. This pattern is repeated in lines 3 to 4 and 6 to 7.	It creates a flowing quality that emphasises the idea of one thing flowing into another – e.g. 'winds' (3) and 'emotion' (4) – or harmony and unity.

6 **Possible answer**: … creates a sense of urgency, conveying how much the speaker wishes to see her lover.

Voice and viewpoint [p. 57]

1 The viewpoint in 'Follower' is in the first person and the past tense. The speaker is reflecting on a memory of his father.

2 The speaker in 'Porphyria's Lover' is unreliable. When he strangles Porphyria in lines 39 to 41, we recognise he is unstable, and this realisation has great impact. Previously the speaker had a strong storyteller voice and seemed reliable.

3 The speaker (first person) addresses the lover in the second-person point of view, with 'thee' (17) meaning 'you'. It creates an intimate mood as though the lover was present and the speaker was addressing them directly. This sense of nearness also emphasises the distress the speaker feels.

4 **Possible answer**: The effect of this change is to make the reader feel the intimacy that seems to exist between the speaker and her friend.

Imagery [pp. 58–59]

1 Nature imagery that depicts the weather, landscape and birds.

2 'Eden Rock' uses religious imagery, such as that of the Holy Trinity.

3 We have a glimpse of the physical appearance of the speaker, who wears an apron. In stanza three it is untied, since he has dressed hurriedly after visiting his wife. This image mirrors his attitude to his role as the neglectful shopkeeper.

4 Quotation from 'Walking Away': 'with leaves just turning' (2)

Technique: Metaphor

Effect: The quotation signifies the coming of autumn, a new school year and the loss of summer. It is a metaphor of change for both the child and the father that also implies loss as the child moves to school away from parental care.

Theme: Change and loss

5

Quotation	Technique	Effect
'Straight and slight as a young larch tree' (31) 'The Farmer's Bride'	Simile	Conveys the nature of the bride, who is like a sapling – young, but fragile. The nature imagery that describes her becomes a motif throughout the poem.
'moon' (50) 'Singh Song!'	Symbol	A universal symbol that the reader will immediately associate with romantic love

6 Possible answer: The image suggests the fear of a wild animal being hunted and caught, not a human being, making us feel how inferior the wife's position is.

Poetic devices [pp. 60–61]

1 The theme is coming together, or unity.

2 The phrase 'me with my heartful of headlines' (7) is ambiguous, in that it carries several implied meanings. The quotation is ambiguous because it could mean that:

a) the headlines are emotionally troubling

b) the speaker is tired of writing headlines as part of news stories.

3 The poem opens with the description of a dangerous storm. This is contrasted with the warmth of the cottage. Ironically, Browning reveals that the danger is within the cottage, where Porphyria is murdered, not outside.

4 A rhetorical question is used. No answer is expected from the person addressed. It is used to emphasise the point the speaker is presenting. Example: 'How should I greet thee?' (31) accentuates the speaker's sense of loss. The speaker answers the question in the next and final line.

5

Technique	Quotation/example	Effect
Pathetic fallacy/personification ('Neutral Tones' first stanza)	'starving sod' (3)	Gives the earth or soil human qualities, emphasising how the relationship is dying from the lack of emotional nourishment or love.
Image	'where you sparkle and waltz and laugh before you were mine' from 'Before You Were Mine'.	The image emphasises the idea of a carefree youth before the responsibilities of parenthood. 'sparkle' in particular suggests a bright short-lived moment, emphasising the transient nature of youth.

6 Possible answer: Although 'warm ice' is a contradiction (an oxymoron), it creates the effect that the speaker can feel his grandfather's warmth and nearness, even though he is dead or cold like 'ice'.

Tone and mood [p. 62]

1 Possible answers: joyful, exuberant, enraptured, elated, 'full of delight and energy'

2 The philosophical mood expresses wisdom about the inevitability of a child becoming their own person and detaching from the parents. However, there is also a sense of sadness in this recognition related to the pain of separation.

3 Quotation from 'Singh Song!: 'she effing at my mum/in all di colours of Punjabi' (23, 24)

Mood: Comic and startling

Effect: The metaphor draws on the vivid colours of the Punjab region in India and the Punjabi language to describe the wife's colourful swearing. It conjures up a comic picture in the reader's mind, because it creates surprise through challenging the stereotype of the submissive Asian wife.

4 Possible answer: The first word of the metaphor – 'icebergs' – suggests coldness. It reflects the mood created at the beginning of the poem when the couple are apart and the relationship seems bleak. Contrastingly, 'feather' conveys softness, suggesting that the coldness between the couple is disappearing. The image reflects the opposing moods of the relationship.

PART FIVE: COMPARING POEMS [PP. 64–68]

Evaluating poems [p. 64]

1 Reading activity: no answer required.

2 The natural world

3 Possible answer: The earth is 'waterlogged' in 'Winter Swans', reinforcing the idea that the relationship between the speaker and his partner has foundered. We therefore assume a quarrel has taken place between the couple. However, in 'Eden Rock' the stream is described as 'drifted', as if it is flowing leisurely. The image creates a sense of happiness and we feel that the speaker is recalling a hopeful memory of family love. In both 'Winter Swans' and Eden Rock' the poets use images of the natural world to present human relationships.

Using connectives [p. 65]

1 The young wife in 'The Farmer's Bride' does not conform to the Victorian idea of what a wife is supposed to be. **Although** she does her domestic duties as expected, she tries her best to avoid relations with her husband. She is seen as odd, as if she was 'not a woman'. **However** her extreme fear of 'men-folk' in general suggests former abuse that has not been recognised. **Since** she has no power there is little she can do. **Instead**, the only way she can act is to try and escape. **In contrast** the speaker in 'Sonnet 29 – "I think of thee!"' fits the idea of what a Victorian woman should be. She is like the clinging 'vine' who exists 'within' her lover's 'shadow'. **In addition**, and to reinforce the difference, the male lover is described as the strong 'palm-tree'.

2 Possible answer: **Unlike** 'The Farmer's Bride' and 'Sonnet 29 – "I think of thee!"', 'Singh Song!' is a modern poem and the wife behaves very differently as a 'newly bride'. **For example**, she chooses her own style of dress and is not governed by convention. **Above all**, she pursues her own interests as she logs into her 'Sikh lover' website, **whereas** neither the farmer's wife nor the speaker in 'Sonnet 29 – "I think of thee!"' appear to have any real independence.

Using quotations [p. 66]

1 The speaker in 'Follower' looks back at his childhood and recalls his father working the **'horse-plough'**. He remembers how his father turned the earth over **'without breaking'** it, a perfect action that reveals what **'An expert'** his father was. Unlike the rural setting in 'Follower', 'Before You Were Mine' has an urban setting. Here the speaker imagines a time **'ten years'** before she was born. In her imagination she sees her mother as a young glamorous woman in a **'polka-dot dress'** or making her way across **'George Square'** in Glasgow.

2 **Possible answers**:

Porphyria arrives at the cottage in disarray and removes her 'dripping cloak and shawl', suggesting that as a Victorian woman she is unlikely to be poor if she owns both.

At the end of the poem the speaker looks out 'on an endless sky' when he opens the window hatch in the attic, implying that the panoramic view represents an image of freedom.

A rhetorical question 'If they kiss not me?' is asked at the end of the poem and suggests that the speaker is trying to seduce the person to whom the poem is addressed.

Writing a comparison [p. 67]

1 Compare how **poets present ideas** about **betrayal** in relationships in 'When We Two Parted' and 'Neutral Tones'.

2 **Possible answer: Both** poets present ideas about betrayal through their speakers. In 'When We Two Parted' and 'Neutral Tones' the poets depict love as difficult and hurtful. **For example, in** the former poem the speaker describes his sense of deep betrayal when he accuses the loved one directly of breaking her 'vows' to him. **In the same way** the speaker in 'Neutral Tones' feels betrayed not only by the person he once loved, but also by love itself, which 'deceives', as if neither have lived up to his expectations. **So,** both speakers are disappointed in love and there is no hint in either poem of any hope for the future.

PART SIX: PROGRESS BOOSTER

Key skills and using quotations [pp. 69–70]

2 **Student A:** Level – Mid

Why? The student identifies an important moment in the poem and offers a short analysis. A quotation is given but the technique used is not mentioned, and for greater fluency the quotation should be embedded more successfully in a sentence.

Student B: Level – High

Why? The student writes fluently, quotations are successfully embedded and the poetic techniques mentioned are used correctly and appropriately. The analysis is convincing and developed.

3, 4 Quotation 2 opens the poem and refers to an event from the past, the time of which is recalled precisely, so both these features suggest the memory will be important in the poem.

5 … they are all still painful events. Their pain is emphasised by the use of 'scorching' as though we were burnt by them.

6 When the farmer in 'The Farmer's Wife' states that 'I've hardly heard her speak at all', it suggests that there is little or no love between the farmer and his wife. However, in 'Sonnet 29 – "I think of thee!"', the speaker's 'thoughts do twine and bud' around her lover, suggesting a deep love.

Using structure and paragraphs effectively [pp. 71–72]

1 Topic sentence: Mew presents the character of the farmer partly through voice and dialect.

Words from quotation: 'bide' and 'woo'

Explanation of words: The dismissive way he uses the verbs … suggests that for him, as a hard-working farmer, marriage is more of a contract than about love.

2 Possible answer: Mew presents the farmer's wife as a shy young woman and an outsider, more at home with animals than humans. The simile 'flying like a hare' depicts her as desperate to escape from the farmer and local people who pursue her. Here, the use of the word 'hare' is powerful. It portrays her not just as an animal, but also as a hunted one.

Topic sentence: Mew presents the farmer's wife as a shy young woman and an outsider, more at home with animals than humans.

Phrase from quotation: 'flying like a hare'

Explanation of words: depicts her as desperate to escape from the farmer and local people who pursue her … portrays her not just as an animal, but also as a hunted one

3 Topic sentence: Armitage presents the son's attempts to break away from his mother's control in stanza one through images that portray freedom.

First quotation: 'prairies of the floors'

Linking sentence: This contrasts with the confined space of a house interior.

Words signalling change or link: This contrasts with; when the son

4 Possible answer: Shelley argues that everything in nature is united. At the beginning of the poem the speaker draws links with a range of natural features that combine, so that for instance, 'fountains mingle with the river' and 'rivers with Oceans'. The verb 'mingle' conveys an easy, natural coming together. Consequently, the speaker asks at the end of the first octave, if this is a natural process, why would the potential lover not wish to unite with the speaker?

Making inferences and interpretations [p. 73]

1 Topic sentence: The speaker imagines that before she was born, her mother's life in the city as a young woman was glamorous and thrilling.

Development of first point: The vibrant nightlife is conjured up through the image of 'the ballroom with the thousand eyes' …

Sentence with inference/exploration: However through connotations of light, the image also suggests the light in the dancers' eyes and makes associations with the bright lights of the city and youthful excitement.

2 c) Why? The poet brings together the senses of sight and smell through the key words 'clear' and 'scent' to create an intense image, suggesting the intense love the speaker feels for her mother.

Writing about context [p. 74]

1 Her choices suggest a multicultural Britain, rather than the stereotypical view that all Sikh wives wear the same kind of clothes.

2 b) 'in di worst Indian shop/on di whole Indian road –' reveals the speaker's lack of interest in making money and challenges the stereotype of the Asian shopkeeper.

3 **Possible answer:** The title the poet has chosen, 'Singh Song!', also has a contextual reference. It is a pun. It plays with the name given to Sikh men, 'Singh'. The expression 'sing song' is also a common English expression that refers to the cadence of a voice that has a marked rise and fall. The term can be used as an insult. Here the poet uses it ironically to challenge the stereotype that English Punjabi speakers have such voices. He takes possession of the insult and, through the title, mocks it.

ANSWERS

Sample answers [pp. 77–82]

1 A

4 **Student A**: Level – Mid

Why? The student has focused on an important point and presented it clearly and quotations are successfully contained in the sentence. Some explanation of imagery is offered, but it is not developed and interpretation is limited.

Student B: Level – High

Why? The student interprets the imagery extremely well, writes fluently, embeds quotations successfully and makes convincing links to other parts of the poem.

6 Summing-up sentence: Both poems, then, explore the ties that bind father and son, but which are inevitably broken as time progresses.

Points suggesting differences: but as 'Follower' suggests …'; The different perspectives …

Final recap sentence: The different perspectives … both reveal this pain of letting go through the act of walking – as the child leaves the waiting father behind at the school gates, or watches the father 'stumbling' in his tracks.

Final quotation: 'stumbling' from 'Follower'

8 a) It makes no comparisons between the poems.

b) It does not give any interpretations.

c) No quotations are included.

10 a) It notes similarities and differences between the poems.

b) It uses quotations and embeds them in a sentence.

c) It refers to poetic techniques.

13 The sample response provided is a High level response because it:

- compares poems in a detailed and well-structured way, moving fluently between ideas in the two poems

- offers convincing ideas and different interpretations and perspectives on the poems

- analyses and explores the poets' methods and effects with insight, and a sound knowledge of poetic terminology

- includes well-chosen quotations and references and embeds them fluently in sentences.